Solving Problems in Vibrations

Solving Problems in Vibrations

J. S. Anderson B.Sc.(Eng), Ph.D., A.K.C., C.Eng., M.R.Ae.S.
Department of Mechanical Engineering,
The City University, London

M. Bratos-Anderson M.Sc., Dr.Tech.Sc.
Department of Mechanical Engineering,
The City University, London

Longman Scientific and Technical,
Longman Group UK Limited,
Longman House, Burnt Mill, Harlow
Essex CM20 2JE, England
and Associated Companies throughout the world.

First published 1987

British Library Cataloguing in Publication Data

Anderson, J. S.
  Solving problems in vibrations.—
  (Solving problems series)
  1. Machinery—Vibration   2. Rotational
  motion
  I. Title   II. Bratos-Anderson, M.
  621.8′11   TJ177

ISBN 0-582-99813-1

Produced by Longman Singapore Publishers (Pte) Ltd.
Printed in Singapore

Contents

Contents

Preface

This book has been written to aid students during the second year of study for an engineering degree. The text is mostly concerned with linear systems with a single degree of freedom. A chapter on systems with two degrees of freedom has been included, even though this subject may be studied in the third year of some courses.

Each chapter of the book possesses three distinct parts. Firstly there is some introductory theory giving background to the worked examples which form the second and most important part. Finally, at the end of each chapter, there are exercises to enable the student to obtain experience in solving problems. The worked examples described in this book are mostly based on examination questions. We do not intend to provide model solutions of the kind that the student might hope to provide for his examiners. We aim to show how the principles of mechanics are applied to solving problems in vibration. In many of the worked examples we give a full explanation of each step in the solution procedure. We sometimes provide alternative solutions or digress to discuss interesting aspects of the problem.

In this book the method of solution is mostly through free-body diagrams which are used as an aid to writing the equations of motion. However, in Chapter 4 energy methods are also discussed. In writing the differential equations the 'dot' notation is used to indicate differentiation with respect to time. A bold symbol indicates a vector.

We are indebted to the Registrar of the City University for permission to include examination problems which have previously occurred in examination papers of the University. Many of these examination problems have been written by our colleagues in the Department of Mechanical Engineering at the City University. We have had a wide selection to choose from and we are very grateful to our colleagues for the work they have done over many years. In particular we should like to acknowledge the help of J. E. Cannell, G. T. S. Done, I. W. Graham, H. R. Harrison, B. G. Main, T. Nettleton, D. W. Oates, A. R. D. Thorley, R. G. P. Weighton and L. J. Wilkins.

Finally, we submit this book to our readers with a certain amount of humility. We realize that it is easy for questions to seem contrived and even ridiculous. A cautionary example is quoted by Max Born in his book *My Life: Recollections of a Nobel Laureate*, Scribner's 1978: 'On an elastic bridge stands an elephant of negligible mass; on his trunk sits a mosquito of mass m. Calculate the vibrations of the bridge when the elephant moves the mosquito by rotating his trunk.'

1
Free, undamped vibrations of systems with a single degree of freedom

1.1 Single degree of freedom system

A mechanical system that requires n co-ordinates to define its position at any instant in time is said to have n degrees of freedom. In Figure 1.1(a) the rigid body on the end of the spring can move up or down along the axis YY. This forms a rectilinear system in which one co-ordinate y is required to define the position of the body. The position of the body at any instant is hence defined in terms of the co-ordinate y, and the system is thus said to have one degree of freedom.

In Figure 1.1(b) a rotational system is shown with one degree of freedom. Here a light, elastic shaft, rigidly fixed at one of its ends, supports a rigid flywheel which has a certain moment of inertia. As the shaft twists, a line OA on the flywheel moves to OA' through an angle θ. θ is the one co-ordinate which is sufficient to define the position of every point on the flywheel at any instant in time.

A compound pendulum is also a system with a single degree of freedom. The position of the centre of mass G can be defined if one

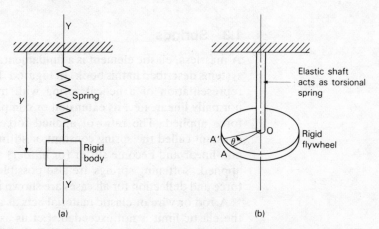

Figure 1.1   System with a single degree of freedom: (a) rectilinear, (b) torsional.

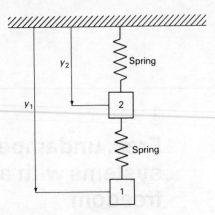

Figure 1.2   System with two degrees of freedom.

co-ordinate is known, namely the angle θ which is the angular displacement of the rigid body (compound pendulum) from its vertical position. See ahead to Figure 1.17 for a diagram of a compound pendulum.

However, the rectilinear system of Figure 1.2 has two degrees of freedom. If the rigid body 1 is displaced downwards or upwards there are still infinitely many possibilities for the position of body 2. Each of the two bodies may move independently in the vertical direction. Two co-ordinates y_1 and y_2 are needed to define the position of the system at any instant of time.

1.2   Undamped system

In this chapter we shall not take into account damping forces which cause energy dissipation in mechanical systems. There will be no loss of energy and once a vibration is started it will be maintained for all time. An undamped system with a single degree of freedom gives rise to a type of motion known as simple harmonic motion, in which the acceleration of the body is proportional to the displacement (y or θ) with negative sign.

1.3   Springs

A massless, elastic element is a fundamental component in the vibrating systems described in this book. In Figure 1.1(a) there is a diagrammatical representation of a helical spring with metal coils. Such a spring is normally linear, i.e., its extension or compression is proportional to the force applied. The ratio of applied force to resulting deflection is a constant called the spring constant or stiffness. Most rubber springs are non-linear and become stiffer (or harder) as a sufficiently large force is applied. Softening springs are also possible. The relationships between force and deflection for all cases are shown in Figure 1.3.

A rod or wire of elastic material acts as a linear spring, provided that the elastic limit is not exceeded. Let us assume that when a force F is applied along the axis of the rod or wire there is an extension or

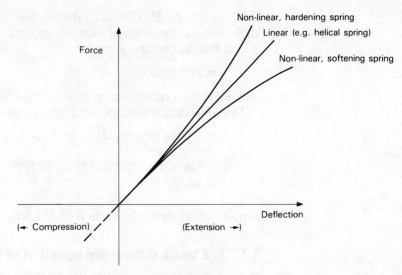

Force

(← Compression)

Deflection

(Extension →)

Figure 1.3   Force–deflection relationships for different springs.

compression y. The ratio F/y is the stiffness of the rod and is related to cross-sectional area A of the rod, its length l and Young's modulus E, a characteristic factor of the elastic material, in the following way:

$$\text{stiffness} = F/y = EA/l \qquad (\text{units} - \text{N/m}),$$

where

$$E = \text{stress/strain} = (F/A)/(y/l) = Fl/yA.$$

Similarly, a torsional spring in a rotational system (Figure 1.1(b)) has a rotational stiffness which is provided by the shaft (or wire) as it twists about its axis. This torsional stiffness is defined as the ratio of a torque T to an angle of twist θ induced in the shaft by the torque, and is given by:

$$T/\theta = GI_p/l \qquad (\text{units} - \text{N m/rad}),$$

where G is the modulus of rigidity, I_p is the polar second moment of area ($\pi d^4/32$ for a wire or circular solid shaft of diameter d) and l is the length of the wire or shaft which is twisting.

Example 1.1
Stiffness of beam

A wooden beam of length 2 m is simply supported at its ends. The beam is rectangular in cross-section, 300 mm wide by 30 mm thick. Young's modulus E is 11×10^9 Pa. If a concentrated load of 300 kg is attached to the beam at the middle what is the equivalent stiffness of the beam?

Solution   A standard textbook on strength of materials (for example, *Mechanics of Solids and Structures* by P. P. Benham and F. V. Warnock (2nd edn), Pitmans 1973, or *Strength of Materials and Structures* by

J. Case and A. H. Chilver, Edward Arnold 1971) will state that the deflection y at the centre of a simply supported beam of length l caused by a load F at the centre is given by:

$$y = Fl^3/(48EI),$$

where I is the second moment of area of the beam cross-section.

The equivalent stiffness $k = 48EI/l^3$. In this example,

$$I = (300 \times 30)(30^2/12) \times 10^{-12} \text{ m}^4$$
$$= 675 \times 10^{-9} \text{ m}^4,$$
$$k = (48 \times 11 \times 10^9 \times 675 \times 10^{-9})/2^3$$
$$= 44.55 \text{ kN/m}.$$

Answer Stiffness of the beam is **44.55 kN/m.**

1.4 The basic differential equation of the motion

The spring mass system of Figure 1.1(a) is a basic arrangement. In the static equilibrium position the spring of stiffness k is extended by y_0 and the forces acting on the body are shown in Figure 1.4(a).

For the case of static equilibrium (see the free body diagram of Figure 1.4(a)):

$$mg - ky_0 = 0.$$

If the body is displaced by, for example, y, downwards from the equilibrium position, the forces are now as shown in Figure 1.4(b). There is no longer static equilibrium and the body accelerates. Applying Newton's second law, we obtain the following differential equation of motion of the system:

$$mg - k(y_0 + y) = m\ddot{y}$$

and finally

$$-ky = m\ddot{y}, \qquad\qquad [1.1]$$

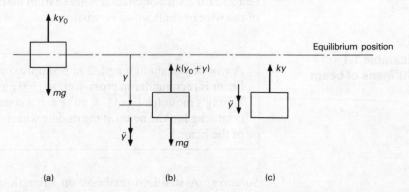

Figure 1.4 Free-body diagrams for body on spring: (a) in static equilibrium; (b) dynamic case showing all forces; (c) dynamic case showing only oscillating force.

which is the equation for simple harmonic motion and can be written as:

$$\ddot{y} + (k/m)y = 0. \qquad [1.2]$$

Equation (1.2) is a linear, second-order differential equation with constant coefficients.

For a given system the ratio k/m may be denoted by ω_n^2 so that we have:

$$\ddot{y} + \omega_n^2 y = 0. \qquad [1.3]$$

ω_n is called the undamped circular natural frequency and has the units of rad/s. It should not be confused with f_n, the undamped natural frequency, which has units of Hz (an abbreviation for hertz and previously known as cycles/second). With or without subscripts ω and f are related by the following expression:

$$\omega = 2\pi f.$$

You may find other expressions for circular frequency, such as angular frequency, radiancy or pulsatance.

It is possible to write down equation [1.1] immediately by analysing the free body diagram in Figure 1.4(c). The forces mg and ky_0 exist all the time, and always cancel each other out. Equation [1.1] only contains terms whose values oscillate during the vibration. In general solutions will be obtained more quickly by omitting these constant forces. However, there are some problems where the weight needs to be considered: for example, in problems involving inverted or compound pendula. In these cases the moment of the weight is varying.

1.5 Solution of the differential equation

The general solution of equation [1.3] is known to be in terms of trigonometric functions and two arbitrary constants. Thus,

$$y = A \cos \omega_n t + B \sin \omega_n t. \qquad [1.4]$$

An alternative formula is:

$$y = X \cos (\omega_n t - \Phi), \qquad [1.5]$$

where the two constants are now the amplitude $X \, (= (A^2 + B^2)^{0.5})$ and the phase angle $\Phi \, (= \tan^{-1} B/A)$.

The values of the constants must be found from the initial conditions. Thus at $t = 0$ we need to know the values of y and $\dot{y}$, as two separate initial conditions are required for a second-order differential equation.

Example 1.2
Mass–spring system with different initial conditions

A body of mass 4 kg is supported on springs which have an equivalent stiffness of 2500 N/m. (a) The mass is initially displaced downwards by 100 mm from the equilibrium position and then released. (b) The body is struck by an impulse of 10 N s which acts vertically downwards. In both cases determine the expressions for the displacements.

Solution The diagrams of Figure 1.4 apply, so they will not be repeated. $m = 4$ kg and $k = 2500$ N/m, hence $\omega_n^2 = 625$ and $\omega_n = 25$ rad/s. Equation [1.3] becomes now:

$$\ddot{y} + 625y = 0$$

and the general solution of this equation is:

$$y = A \cos 25t + B \sin 25t, \qquad\qquad\qquad [1.6]$$

where y is the displacement of the body from the static rest position. An expression for the velocity is obtained by differentiating the above equation [1.6]. Hence,

$$\dot{y} = -25A \sin 25t + 25B \cos 25t. \qquad\qquad [1.7]$$

(a) For $t = 0$, $y = 0.1$ m.

From equation [1.6],

$$0.1 = A + 0$$

and

$$A = 0.1.$$

As the body was initially at rest, for $t = 0$, $\dot{y} = 0$. From equation [1.7],

$$0 = 0 + 25B$$

and

$$B = 0.$$

The expression for the displacement is finally:

$$y = 0.1 \cos 25t.$$

Comparing the above expression for the displacement with equation [1.5] one can deduce that the amplitude is 0.1 m and the phase angle is 0.

(b) $t = 0$, $y = 0$ because the body is not displaced during the application of the impulse (remember an impulse exists for a very short time).

From equation [1.6],

$$0 = A + 0$$

and

$$A = 0.$$

The integration of Newton's second law with respect to time leads to the relation:

$$\text{Impulse} = \text{change in momentum}$$

Hence,

$$10 = 4(\dot{y}(0) - 0),$$

where $\dot{y}(0)$ is the velocity immediately after the impact. Therefore, $\dot{y}(0) = 2.5$ m/s.

From equation [1.7], for $t = 0$

$$2.5 = 25B$$

and

$$B = 0.1.$$

Therefore,

$$y = 0.1 \sin 25t$$

or

$$y = 0.1 \cos (25t - \pi/2).$$

In this case (with the cosine) the amplitude is still 0.1 m, and by comparing with equation [1.5] it can be seen that the phase angle is 90°. The displacement discussed in part (b) lags by a phase angle of 90° the displacement obtained in part (a), as shown in Figure 1.5.

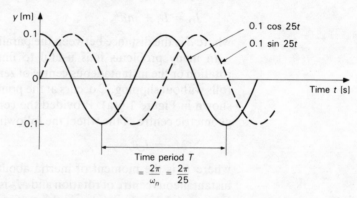

Figure 1.5   Displacement against time for spring–mass system.

1.6   The plane-motion equations

So far we have mostly been concerned with the rectilinear motion of a body on a spring. Many problems in this book will deal with plane motion or motion in two dimensions. The three equations that describe the dynamics of a rigid body in a plane (xy) are derived from Newton's laws of motion and are:

$$\Sigma F_x = m\ddot{x}_G \quad (\Sigma F_x, \text{ force components in } x \text{ direction}) \qquad [1.8]$$

$$\Sigma F_y = m\ddot{y}_G \quad (\Sigma F_y, \text{ force components in } y \text{ direction}) \qquad [1.9]$$

$$\Sigma M_G = I_G\ddot{\theta} \quad (\Sigma M_G, \text{ moments about the rotation axis through}$$

$$\text{the centre of mass G}). \qquad [1.10]$$

where the body has mass m and moment of inertia I_G about the rotation axis through the centre of mass G (perpendicular to the xy plane). The moments are about the same axis. Note that the term rotation axis here is defined as an axis perpendicular to the plane of motion of the rigid body. The position of the centre of mass G of the body has the co-ordinates (x_G, y_G). The components of acceleration of G in the x and y directions are $\ddot{x}_G$ and $\ddot{y}_G$, respectively. The angular acceleration of the body is $\ddot{\theta}$. Further details on these equations and their applications may be obtained from books on mechanics such as *Dynamics* by J. L. Meriam (2nd edn), Wiley 1975, or *Principles of Engineering Mechanics* by H. R. Harrison and T. Nettleton, Edward Arnold 1978. When there is rotation of a rigid body about a fixed axis through point O one may take moments about the fixed rotation axis, so the equation of motion is:

$$\Sigma M_O = I_O \ddot{\theta}, \tag{1.11}$$

where I_O is the moment of inertia of the rigid body about the axis of rotation through O. In fact equation [1.11] also applies when, e.g., the axis has a constant velocity.

The parallel-axes theorem is used to relate I_O and I_G.

$$I_O = I_G + md^2, \tag{1.12}$$

where d is the distance between the parallel axes through O and G.

In many problems it is useful to find the instantaneous centre of rotation or the instantaneous centre of zero velocity, C. For a wheel, that rolls without slipping, C occurs at the point of contact with the ground, as shown in Figure 1.6(a). Provided the centre of mass coincides with the geometric centre of the wheel the following equation is allowed:

$$\Sigma M_C = I_C \ddot{\theta}, \tag{1.13}$$

where I_C is the moment of inertia about the rotation axis through the instantaneous centre of rotation and M_C is a moment about the same axis. Equation [1.13] also applies in the case of a spool unwinding from a rope, where C is located as shown in Figure 1.6(b).

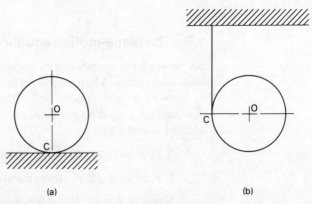

(a) (b)

Figure 1.6 Location of instantaneous centre C for (a) rolling wheel, (b) spool unwinding.

Example 1.3
Natural frequency of a
system with rolling

Determine the undamped natural frequency of small oscillations of the system shown in Figure 1.7(a). The uniform disc of mass m has two springs attached as indicated. Assume that the disc rolls without slipping.

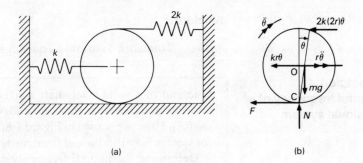

(a)   (b)

Figure 1.7   (a) Diagram for Example 1.3; (b) free-body diagram for disc in Example 1.3.

Solution   As the wheel rolls on the horizontal surface the displacement of the centre of the wheel is $r\theta$. The spring of stiffness $2k$ is attached to a point on the top of the wheel. The horizontal component of the displacement of this point is approximately $2r\theta$ for small oscillations. The point on the wheel in contact with the surface is the instantaneous centre of rotation C. This point is shown on the free-body diagram of Figure 1.7(b). If we take moments about the axis of rotation through C the only forces that are involved are the two spring forces, provided the angle θ is small.

I_G for a uniform disc about the axis through its mass centre is $mr^2/2$; hence by equation [1.12]:

$$I_C = mr^2/2 + mr^2.$$

It should be noted that the centre of mass coincides with the geometrical centre of the disc. Therefore, equation [1.13] leads to:

$$-2r(4kr\theta) - r(kr\theta) = 1.5mr^2\ddot{\theta}$$

or

$$-9kr^2\theta = 1.5mr^2\ddot{\theta}$$

or

$$\ddot{\theta} + (6k/m)\theta = 0,$$

$$\omega_n = (6k/m)^{0.5},$$

and

$$f_n = \{1/(2\pi)\}(6k/m)^{0.5}.$$

The same result may be obtained by using equations [1.8] and [1.10]:

$$-F - kr\theta - 4kr\theta = mr\ddot{\theta},$$
$$+Fr - r(4kr\theta) = I_G\ddot{\theta}.$$

Multiplying the first equation by r and adding give:

$$-9kr^2\theta = 1.5mr^2\ddot{\theta},$$

as before.

Answer Undamped natural frequency is $\{1/(2\pi)\}(6k/m)^{0.5}$.

**Example 1.4
Natural frequency of a
torsional system**

One end of a solid steel shaft is fixed and a uniform steel disc is attached at its centre to the other end of the shaft. Dimensions of the shaft and disc are shown in Figure 1.8(a). The modulus of rigidity G for steel is 8×10^{10} Pa and the density of steel is 7.8×10^3 kg/m³.

Determine the natural frequency of torsional oscillations of the system.

Solution Moment of inertia I of the disc about the XX axis is $0.5mr^2$ or

$$I = 0.5(7.8 \times 10^3 \times \pi \times 0.090^2 \times 0.005)(0.090)^2$$
$$= 4.019 \times 10^{-3} \text{ kg m}^2.$$

Torsional stiffness s of the shaft is given by:

$$s = GI_p/l = 8 \times 10^{10}(\pi \times 0.012^4/32)/0.2$$
$$= 814.3 \text{ N m}.$$

The free-body diagram for the disc is shown in Figure 1.8(b). From equation [1.11]:

$$-s\theta = I\ddot{\theta}$$

or

$$\ddot{\theta} + \{814.3/(4.019 \times 10^{-3})\}\theta = 0.$$

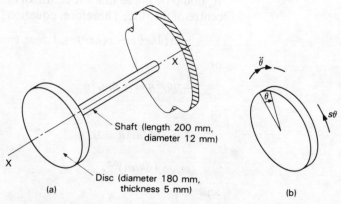

Shaft (length 200 mm, diameter 12 mm)

Disc (diameter 180 mm, thickness 5 mm)

(a)

(b)

Figure 1.8   (a) Diagram for Example 1.4; (b) torque and angular acceleration on the disc.

Hence,

$$\omega_n = 450.13 \text{ rad/s} \quad \text{or} \quad f_n = 71.64 \text{ Hz}.$$

Answer   Natural frequency of torsional oscillations is **71.6 Hz.**

Note that we have neglected the mass of the shaft in this problem. The mass of the shaft is 0.1778 that of the disc.

Example 1.5
System with instantaneous centre of rotation

In Figure 1.9 the pulley has a mass of 20 kg and a radius of gyration about its centre k_G of 300 mm. The spring has a stiffness of 500 N/m. A load of 25 kg hangs from the centre of the pulley.

Determine the natural frequency of vertical vibrations when the load is released from a displaced position.

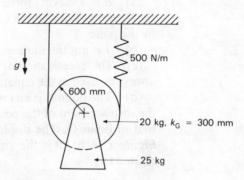

Figure 1.9   Diagram for Example 1.5.

Solution   We will first of all consider the system in static equilibrium. Figure 1.10 gives the appropriate free-body diagram for the pulley and

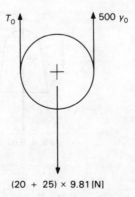

Figure 1.10   Free-body diagram of drum in static equilibrium (Example 1.5).

load. y_0 is the initial extension of the spring. In static equilibrium the right-hand sides of equations [1.9] and [1.10] are now zero, hence

$$45 \times 9.81 - T_0 - 500y_0 = 0,$$
$$0.6 \times T_0 - 0.6 \times 500y_0 = 0.$$

So

$$1000y_0 = 45 \times 9.81. \qquad [1.14]$$

Next the load is displaced downwards by y. The new free-body diagram for the load is given in Figure 1.11(a).

$$\Sigma F_y = m\ddot{y}_G, \qquad \text{hence} \quad 25 \times 9.81 - R = 25\ddot{y}. \qquad [1.15]$$

The free-body diagram for the pulley is shown in Figure 1.11(b), and there are several points that should be noted about these free-body diagrams.

(a) R is a varying force of contact that the load exerts on the pulley. By Newton's third law an equal and opposite force is exerted on the load by the pulley.

(b) T is not the same as T_0.

(c)   The acceleration of the centre of mass of the pulley at O should always be used in the equation of motion.

(d)   The point C is an instantaneous centre of zero velocity and hence the displacement of the point of attachment of the spring is $2y$, or twice that of point O. The displacement profile of the pulley is indicated in Figure 1.11(b). θ is the angle through which the pulley rotates and is related to y by

$$y = 0.6\theta,$$

and also

$$\ddot{y} = 0.6\ddot{\theta}. \qquad [1.16]$$

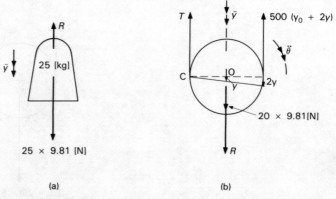

(a)   (b)

Figure 1.11   Example 1.5. Free-body diagrams showing all forces for (a) load of 25 kg and (b) drum.

From equations [1.9] and [1.10]:

$$-T + R + 20 \times 9.81 - 500(y_0 + 2y) = 20\ddot{y}, \qquad [1.17]$$
$$0.6T - 0.6 \times 500 \times (y_0 + 2y) = 20 \times 0.3^2\ddot{\theta}. \qquad [1.18]$$

Elimination of T from equations [1.17] and [1.18] and substitution for $\ddot{\theta}$ from [1.16] lead to:

$$R - 1000(y_0 + 2y) + 20 \times 9.81 = 25\ddot{y}.$$

Elimination of R using equation [1.15] gives:

$$-1000(y_0 + 2y) + 45 \times 9.81 = 50\ddot{y}.$$

Finally, y_0, the initial spring extension, is eliminated using the static equilibrium equation [1.14].

$$-1000 \times 2y = 50\ddot{y},$$

or

$$\ddot{y} + 40y = 0. \qquad [1.19]$$

So $\omega_n^2 = 40$, $\omega_n = 6.32$ rad/s, $f_n = 1.01$ Hz.

Answer   Undamped natural frequency is **1.01 Hz.**

A solution is achieved more quickly if we disregard the steady forces, realize straight away that C is the instantaneous centre of rotation and consider the pulley and load combined so that force R is eliminated. The only free-body diagram we need now is shown in Figure 1.12. In this case we can use equation [1.13]:

$$\Sigma M_C = I_C\ddot{\theta}.$$

(Note that this would not be correct if the centre of mass did not coincide with the geometric centre O.)

$$I_C = 20(0.3^2 + 0.6^2) + 25 \times 0.6^2$$
$$\text{(pulley)} \qquad \text{(load)}$$
$$= 18 \text{ kg m}^2.$$

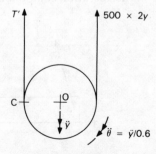

Figure 1.12   Example 1.5. Free-body diagram for drum, showing only the oscillating forces.

Hence

$$-1.2(500 \times 2y) = 18y/0.6,$$

and

$$\ddot{y} + 40y = 0,$$

as obtained before (equation [1.19]).

**Example 1.6
System with
curvilinear translation**

Figure 1.13 shows a uniform, rigid beam of mass m supported horizontally at its ends by two light, parallel links of equal lengths l. If the beam is given a small displacement and released, obtain an expression for the natural frequency of the resulting oscillations.

If the links oscillate with an amplitude of θ_0 radians, obtain approximate expressions for the tensions in the links when they are (a) in a vertical position and (b) inclined at an angle θ_0 to the vertical (Take into account second-order terms.)

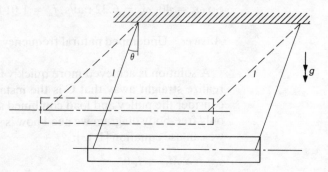

Figure 1.13   Example 1.6. Curvilinear translation of a beam.

Solution   The beam executes curvilinear translation. As may be seen from the dotted outline in Figure 1.13, the beam is always horizontal and has no rotation. Point A on the link has normal and tangential acceleration components $l\dot{\theta}^2$ and $l\ddot{\theta}$, respectively. B and hence G have the same acceleration components, as shown in Figure 1.14. As the beam does not

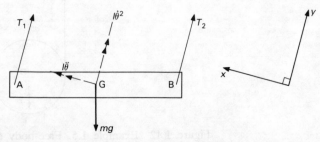

Figure 1.14   Free-body diagrams for beam in curvilinear translation.

rotate the moments about an axis through G are zero and, therefore

$$T_1 = T_2 = T.$$

Note also that there are no components of force at A or B perpendicular to the links because the links are light.

$$(\Sigma F_x = m\ddot{x}_G) \qquad - mg \sin \theta = ml\ddot{\theta}.$$

For small oscillations $\sin \theta = \theta$.

Therefore,

$$\ddot{\theta} + (g/l)\theta = 0$$

and hence

$$\omega_n = (g/l)^{0.5},$$

which is the same expression as for a simple pendulum.

Answer   Natural frequency is given by $(0.5/\pi)(g/l)^{0.5}$.

To find the tensions in the links we apply equation [1.9]: $\Sigma F_y = m\ddot{y}_G$.

$$2T - mg \cos \theta = ml\dot{\theta}^2$$

and if θ is small (second-order terms included):

$$T = ml\dot{\theta}^2/2 + (mg/2)(1 - \theta^2/2).$$

Because

$$\theta = \theta_0 \sin \omega_n t \qquad \text{and} \qquad \dot{\theta} = \omega_n \theta_0 \cos \omega_n t$$

then

$$T = 0.5ml\omega_n^2\theta_0^2 \cos^2 \omega_n t + 0.5mg(1 - 0.5\theta_0^2 \sin^2 \omega_n t).$$

(a)   In the vertical position $\theta = 0$ or $\sin \omega_n t = 0$ and $\cos \omega_n t = 1$. Therefore,

$$T = \theta_0^2 ml\omega_n^2/2 + mg/2,$$

but

$$\omega_n^2 = g/l$$

and

$$T = 0.5mg(1 + \theta_0^2).$$

(b)   With the links at θ_0 to the vertical, $\theta = \theta_0$. Thus

$$\sin \omega_n t = 1 \qquad \text{and} \qquad \cos \omega_n t = 0.$$

Therefore,

$$T = 0.5mg(1 - 0.5\theta_0^2).$$

Answer (a) $T = 0.5mg(1 + \theta_0^2)$.

(b) $T = 0.5mg(1 - 0.5\theta_0^2)$.

Example 1.7 **Trifilar suspension**	The trifilar suspension provides a method of measuring the moment of inertia of a body about an axis passing vertically through its mass centre. The apparatus consists of a circular platform suspended by three equi-spaced wires of equal length which are rigidly fixed at their upper ends, as shown in Figure 1.15. The body under consideration, in this case a connecting rod of an internal combustion engine, is placed with its mass centre exactly over the centre of the platform. The platform is given a small rotational displacement about the vertical axis through its geometrical centre and released. The periodic time T_n of the oscillations is measured and the moment of inertia I, about the vertical axis through the mass centre, is calculated from the following expression:

$$T_n = 2\pi \left\{ \frac{L(I_O + I)}{gr^2(M_O + M)} \right\}^{0.5}, \qquad [1.20]$$

where L = length of the suspension wires,

           r = radius from the centre of the platform to the attachment points of the suspension wires,

           I_O = moment of inertia of the platform, about the vertical axis through the mass centre,

        M_O = mass of the platform,

         M = mass of the body.

Derive the above expression [1.20].

(This apparatus is particularly useful for measuring the moment of inertia of irregularly shaped components, such as the connecting rod, whose moments of inertia cannot be easily calculated from their dimensions. The platform may contain Vee pieces for supporting the components and they should be placed so that the centre of mass of the platform remains at its geometric centre.)

Solution   Figure 1.16(a) shows that when the platform is rotated about its vertical axis through an angle θ the suspension wires rotate through Φ. Hence, provided the angle θ is small:

$$r\theta = L\Phi.$$

If the tension in each wire is T, then its vertical component is $T \cos \Phi$, as shown in Figure 1.16(b). As angle Φ is small, we may write:

$$3T = M_O g.$$

The horizontal component $T \sin \Phi$ is tangential to the circle (of radius r) which passes through the suspension points (see Figure 1.16(c)) and if $\ddot{\theta}$ is

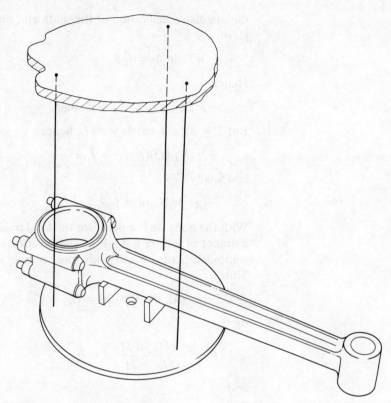

Figure 1.15 Trifilar suspension.

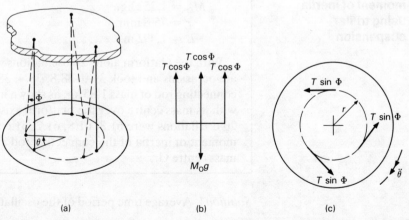

(a)   (b)   (c)

Figure 1.16   Trifilar suspension: (a) rotation of platform; (b) vertical forces on the platform; (c) tangential force components and angular acceleration.

the angular acceleration of the platform, one can obtain from equation [1.10]:

$$-3rT \sin \Phi = I_O\ddot{\theta}.$$

Hence,

$$-3rT\Phi = I_O\ddot{\theta}, \quad \text{as } \Phi \text{ is small.}$$

But $T = M_Og/3$ and $\Phi = r\theta/L$; hence:

$$-3r(M_Og/3)(r\theta/L) = I_O\ddot{\theta}$$

and finally

$$-(gr^2M_O/L)\theta = I_O\ddot{\theta}.$$

With the body on the platform the total mass becomes $M_O + M$ and the moment of inertia is $I_O + I$. The position of the centre of mass of the combined platform and body must remain on the axis of the platform. Thus

$$-[gr^2(M_O + M)/L]\theta = (I_O + I)\ddot{\theta}$$

or

$$\ddot{\theta} + \frac{gr^2(M_O + M)}{L(I_O + I)}\,\theta = 0$$

and

$$\omega_n^2 = gr^2(M_O + M)/\{L(I_O + I)\}.$$

As $T_n = 2\pi/\omega_n$ we obtain equation [1.20].

Answer $\quad T_n = 2\pi[L(I_O + I)/\{gr^2(M_O + M)\}]^{0.5}.$

Example 1.8
Measurement of
moment of inertia
using trifilar
suspension

In a particular trifilar suspension apparatus (see also Example 1.7)

$$M_O = 1.252\,\text{kg},$$
$$r = 75.8\,\text{mm},$$
$$L = 1.492\,\text{m}.$$

With the platform alone 20 oscillations were timed on five separate occasions and took 39.0, 38.8, 38.4, 38.9 and 38.7 s. When the connecting rod of mass 1.85 kg, as shown in Figure 1.15, was placed with its mass centre over the platform axis the times for five sets of 20 oscillations were 61.8, 61.8, 61.2, 61.6 and 61.6 s. Estimate the moment of inertia of the connecting rod about the axis through its mass centre G.

Solution Average time period of the oscillations for the platform

$$= (39.0 + 38.8 + 38.4 + 38.9 + 38.7)/(5 \times 20)$$
$$= 1.938\,\text{s}.$$

Putting I and M equal to zero in equation [1.20] we find:

$$1.938 = 2\pi\{1.492I_O/(0.0758^2 \times 9.81 \times 1.252)\}^{0.5}$$

and

$$I_O = 4.50 \times 10^{-3} \text{ kg m}^2.$$

For the platform and connecting rod the average time period is 3.08 s. Hence,

$$3.08 = 2\pi\left\{\frac{1.492(4.50 \times 10^{-3} + I)}{0.0758^2 \times 9.81(1.252 + 1.850)}\right\}^{0.5},$$

$$I = 0.0237 \text{ kg m}^2.$$

Answer   Moment of inertia of the connecting rod is **0.024 kg m²**.

**Example 1.9
Moment of inertia
from the compound
pendulum method**

The above estimate of the moment of inertia of the connecting rod is to be checked using the compound pendulum method. The connecting rod is supported on a knife edge first from the small end, as shown in Figure 1.17(a), and secondly from the big end. For the case of suspension from the small end 20 oscillations lasted 21.9, 21.6, 21.9, 21.8 and 21.6 s for five separate tests. From the big end the corresponding results were 19.3, 19.9, 19.5, 19.9, 19.5 s. Dimensions of the connecting rod are shown in Figure 1.17(a).

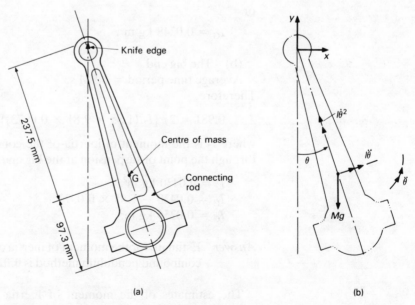

Figure 1.17   (a) Compound pendulum; (b) free-body diagram for compound pendulum.

Solution The free-body diagram for the connecting rod as a compound pendulum is given in Figure 1.17(b). For small oscillations and from equation [1.11]:

$$-Mgl\theta = I_1\ddot{\theta},$$

where I_1 is the moment of inertia about the fixed axis through the point of suspension parallel with the axis through the centre of mass G, and perpendicular to the plane of motion. l is the distance from the centre of mass to the pivot. Hence,

$$\omega_n^2 = Mgl/I_1.$$

And

$$T = 2\pi(I_1/Mgl)^{0.5}.$$

(a) The small end
Average time period $= 1.088$ s.
Therefore,

$$1.088 = 2\pi\{I_1/(1.85 \times 9.81 \times 0.2375)\}^{0.5}.$$

And

$$I_1 = 0.1292 \text{ kg m}^2.$$

From the parallel-axes theorem (equation [1.12]):

$$I_1 = I_G + Ml^2.$$

Thus

$$I_G = 0.1292 - 1.85 \times 0.2375^2$$

or

$$I_G = 0.0248 \text{ kg m}^2.$$

(b) The big end
Average time period $= 0.981$ s.
Therefore,

$$0.981 = 2\pi\{I_2/(1.85 \times 9.81 \times 0.0973)\}^{0.5},$$

where I_2 is the moment of inertia of the connecting rod about the axis through the point of suspension at the big end.

$$I_2 = 0.0430 \text{ kg m}^2,$$
$$I_G = 0.0430 - 1.85 \times 0.0973^2,$$
$$I_G = 0.0255 \text{ kg m}^2.$$

Answer Estimate for the moment of inertia of the connecting rod by the compound pendulum method is **0.025 kg m^2.**

The estimates of the moment of inertia by the trifilar suspension method and by the compound pendulum method are different because of errors in the methods of measurement.

**Example 1.10
System of connected
links**

See Figure 1.18. The mechanism shown consists of a link O_1D which pivots about O_1, a link ALO_2 which is pivoted to O_1D at A, a spring of stiffness k whose ends are attached to the links at C and E respectively and a rigid wheel W whose centre is pinned to the lower link at O_2.

Link O_1D has a mass of 12 kg, mass centre G, and moment of inertia about the pivot (point O_1) of 5 kg m². $O_1A = 0.45$ m, $O_1G = 0.6$ m, $O_1C = 0.9$ m and $O_1D = 1.4$ m.

The masses of link ALO_2 and of wheel W are to be neglected.

In the equilibrium position O_1D and LO_2 are horizontal, E is vertically below C, O_2 is vertically below D, and the spring compression due to the weight of O_1D is 21 mm.

The link O_1D is given a small angular displacement from its equilibrium position and then released.

Determine the value of the natural circular frequency of the ensuing vibrations.

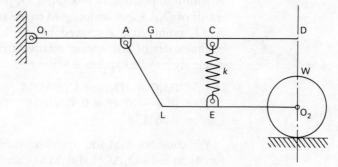

Figure 1.18 Diagram for Example 1.10.

Solution   Figure 1.19 shows the free-body diagrams for the whole assembly and for link $ALEO_2$ in the static equilibrium position. For the whole assembly moments about the axis through O_1 give:

$$1.4R = 0.6 \times 12g.$$

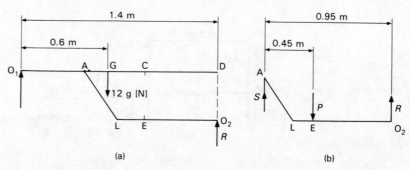

Figure 1.19 Example 1.10. Free-body diagram for the static equilibrium of (a) the whole assembly; (b) the link ALO_2.

For the link $ALEO_2$ moments about an axis through A give:

$$0.95R = 0.45P.$$

Hence

$$P = 0.95 \times 0.6 \times 12g/(1.4 \times 0.45) = 106.5 \text{ N}.$$

As the compression of the spring due to the weight of link O_1D is 21 mm the stiffness k of the spring is given by:

$$k = 106.5/0.021 = 5071.4 \text{ N/m}.$$

The spring is additionally compressed when the link O_1ACD rotates clockwise through an angle θ. The point C is displaced downwards by $O_1C\theta$. At the same time the link ALO_2 rotates through angle Φ anticlockwise. As O_2 maintains the same height, the point E is displaced downwards by $O_2E\Phi$ or $CD\Phi$. Thus the resulting compression of the spring, relative to the equilibrium position, is $O_1C\theta - CD\Phi$. The point A is common to both links O_1ACD and ALO_2. With regard to the static equilibrium position of link O_1ACD, point A has a displacement downwards of $O_1A\theta$, but with regard to the static equilibrium position of link ALO_2 point A is displaced by $AD\Phi$. Thus $O_1A\theta = AD\Phi$ and the compression of the spring relative to its equilibrium position in the assembly may be expressed as:

$$(O_1C - (O_1A \times CD/AD))\theta$$
$$= (0.9 - (0.45 \times 0.5)/0.95)\theta$$
$$= 0.66315\theta.$$

We consider next the dynamic situation and analyse the oscillating forces on links O_1ACD and ALO_2, see Figure 1.20, and write down the equations of motion. Let us take moments about the fixed axis through O_1 for the link O_1ACD ($\Sigma M_O = I_O\ddot{\theta}$):

$$0.45S_1 - 0.9 \times 0.66315k\theta = 5\ddot{\theta}.$$

Similarly, let us take moments about the axis through O_2 for link ALO_2, noting that the link ALO_2 has no mass.

$$0.95S_1 - 0.5 \times 0.66315k\theta = 0.$$

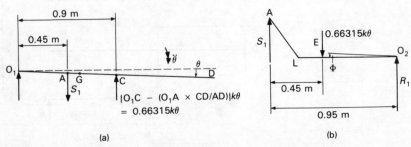

(a)   (b)

Figure 1.20   Example 1.10. Dynamic forces on (a) link O_1ACD and (b) link ALO_2.

From these equations we obtain:

$$(0.45 \times 0.5 \times 0.66315k/0.95)\theta - 0.9 \times 0.66315k\theta = 5\ddot{\theta}$$

or

$$5\ddot{\theta} + 0.43976k\theta = 0.$$

Hence

$$\omega_n^2 = 0.43976 \times 5071.4/5.$$

And

$$\omega_n = 21.12 \text{ rad/s}.$$

Answer The undamped circular natural frequency is **21.12 rad/s.**

**Example 1.11
Kinematics of
connected drums**

In the system shown in Figure 1.21 a belt A is attached to a fixed frame B, wrapped round the drums C and D and supports a load E of 20 kg. The drum C has a mass of 40 kg, radius 150 mm, and radius of gyration about its centre G of 70 mm. Drum D, which is of negligible mass, is attached at its centre to a spring F of stiffness 10 kN/m.

The load E is given a small downwards displacement and released from rest. Determine the natural frequency of the resulting oscillations.

Solution We note that the system is initially in static equilibrium. Let us assume that the load E is given a small downwards displacement x. On the

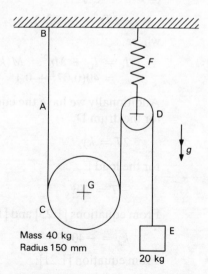

Figure 1.21   Diagram for Example 1.11.

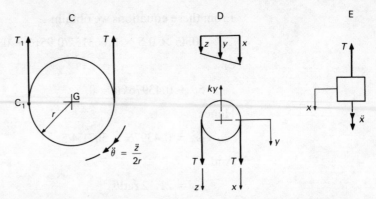

Figure 1.22   Example 1.11. Free-body diagrams for bodies C, D and E.

free-body diagrams for C, D and E in Figure 1.22 are shown the dynamic forces relative to those of static equilibrium. The kinematics of the drum D have to be carefully considered. As the load E is displaced downwards the drum D rotates and the spring is extended. We cannot define the displacement of the centre of drum D in terms of x, so we must denote it by an unknown y. The left part of the drum D has an unknown displacement z. A diagram of the drum displacements is shown above the free-body diagram for drum D. Thus from the kinematics of the drum D we have:

$$y = (x + z)/2. \qquad [1.21]$$

We observe also that the drum C has an instantaneous centre of rotation at point C_1. If the displacement z is, for example, downwards, drum C has a clockwise rotation of $z/2r$, where r is 0.15 m and is the radius of drum C.

Let us take moments about the rotation axis through the instantaneous centre C_1 and write down the equation of motion for the drum C. ($\Sigma M_C = I_C \ddot{\theta}$):

$$-2Tr = I_C(\ddot{z}/2r), \qquad [1.22]$$

where

$$I_C = I_G + Mr^2 = M(k_G^2 + r^2)$$
$$= 40(0.07^2 + 0.15^2) = 1.096 \text{ kg m}^2.$$

Additionally we have the equations,
for the drum D:

$$2T = ky, \qquad [1.23]$$

for the load E:

$$-T = 20\ddot{x}. \qquad [1.24]$$

From equations [1.23] and [1.24]:

$$ky = -40\ddot{x}.$$

From equation [1.21]:

$$x = 2y - z.$$

Hence,
$$ky = -40(2\ddot{y} - \ddot{z}).$$ [1.25]
From equations [1.22] and [1.23]:
$$-kyr = I_C(\ddot{z}/2r).$$
Finally:
$$-2kyr^2 = 1.096\ddot{z}.$$ [1.26]
Let us eliminate $\ddot{z}$ from equations [1.25] and [1.26]:
$$ky = -40(2\ddot{y} + 2kyr^2/1.096)$$
or
$$80\ddot{y} + k(1 + 80r^2/1.096)y = 0.$$
Finally,
$$\ddot{y} + (10\,000(1 + 80 \times 0.15^2/1.096)/80)y = 0.$$
Thus
$$\ddot{y} + 330.3y = 0.$$
Hence
$$\omega_n = 18.17 \text{ rad/s} \quad \text{or} \quad f_n = 2.89 \text{ Hz}.$$

Answer   Natural frequency is **2.89 Hz.**

Note that the system in this example has really two degrees of freedom. However, the motion of this system can be described by one differential equation. The problem has some similarities with Example 6.2, page 178.

**Example 1.12
Natural frequency of
an inverted pendulum**

In the inverted pendulum (see Figure 1.23) a light, rigid rod OA is fixed at O and has a small body of mass M attached at the top. A spring of stiffness k is attached at B so that when the rod AO is in equilibrium in the vertical position the spring is unextended.

If body A is given a small, horizontal displacement, determine the circular frequency of the resulting oscillations.

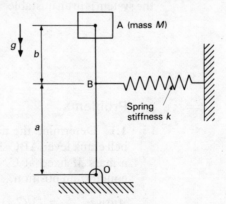

Figure 1.23   Example 1.12. Inverted pendulum.

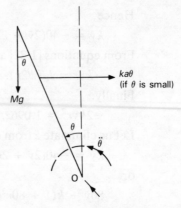

Figure 1.24   Example 1.12. Free-body diagram for inverted pendulum.

Solution   In this problem we must take into account the weight Mg and its moment. When the rod is displaced anti-clockwise through an angle θ, the free-body diagram is as shown in Figure 1.24. Let us take moments about the fixed rotation axis through O and write down the equation of motion for the system:

$$\Sigma M_O = I_O \ddot{\theta}$$
$$Mg(a + b) = \sin\theta - ka\theta = M(a + b)^2\ddot{\theta}.$$

But $\sin\theta = \theta$ for small oscillations, hence

$$(Mg(a + b) - ka)\theta = M(a + b)^2\ddot{\theta}.$$

Finally,

$$\ddot{\theta} + (ka/M(a + b)^2 - g/(a + b))\theta = 0.$$
$$\omega_n = [\{ka/M(a + b)^2\} - g/(a + b)]^{0.5}.$$

Note that if

$$ka/\{M(a + b)^2\} < \{g/(a + b)\}$$

the system is in an unstable state and it simply flops over when disturbed.

Problems

1.1   Determine the natural frequency of small oscillations of the bell crank lever ABC shown in Figure 1.25. The lever is light but has a mass M fixed at C. BC is horizontal when the system is in the equilibrium position.

Answer $f_n = \{1/(2\pi)\}\{(c/d)(k/M)^{0.5}\}$.

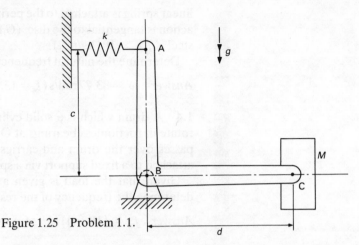

Figure 1.25   Problem 1.1.

1.2   A thin ring of 120 mm radius is placed on a frictionless pivot at O and given a small displacement. Determine the natural frequency of the oscillations. See Figure 1.26.

Answer $\omega_n = 6.39$ rad/s, $f_n = 1.018$ Hz.

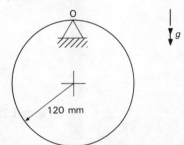

120 mm

Figure 1.26   Problem 1.2.

1.3   A rotational system is formed by a solid steel shaft fixed at one end and a solid steel disc, as shown in Figure 1.27. In addition a

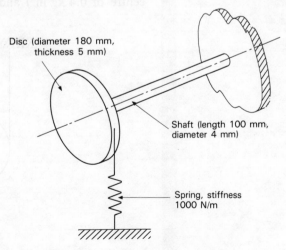

Disc (diameter 180 mm, thickness 5 mm)

Shaft (length 100 mm, diameter 4 mm)

Spring, stiffness 1000 N/m

Figure 1.27   Problem 1.3.

linear spring is attached to the periphery of the disc so that its line of action is tangential to the disc. (G for steel is 8×10^{10} Pa, density of steel is 7.8×10^3 kg/m³.)

Determine the natural frequency of small oscillations.

Answer $\omega_n = 83.77$ rad/s ($f_n = 13.33$ Hz) – mass of shaft neglected.

1.4   A drum which is a solid cylinder of mass m and radius r can rotate in frictionless bearings at O as shown in Figure 1.28. A rope passes over the drum and carries a load of mass M. The rope is attached to a fixed support via a spring of stiffness k.

Given that the load is given a small displacement downwards determine the frequency of the resulting vibrations.

Answer $f_n = \{1/(2\pi)\}\{k/(M + m/2)\}^{0.5}$.

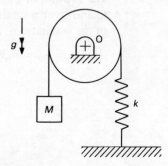

Figure 1.28   Problem 1.4.

1.5   In Figure 1.29 a belt is wrapped round a pulley A (mass 8 kg, radius 120 mm and moment of inertia about an axis through the centre of 0.4 kg m²) and a pulley B (of negligible mass) and is

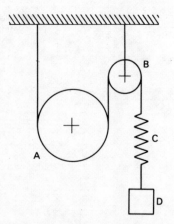

Figure 1.29   Problem 1.5.

attached to a spring C of stiffness 1200 N/m. A load D of mass 4 kg is attached to the spring.

Given that the system is initially in equilibrium and load D is then given a small displacement, estimate the frequency of the vibrations.

Answer $f_n = 3.32$ Hz.

1.6 Figure 1.30 shows an inverted pendulum which is supported vertically in the equilibrium position by two springs, each of stiffness 200 N/m. The distance between the attachment point of each spring and the pivot point O is 240 mm. AB and OC form a rigid inverted T piece.

Determine the natural frequency of small oscillations when

(a) the T piece is of negligible mass and a concentrated mass of 3 kg is placed on OC, 200 mm from O, and

(b) the T piece, with OC equal to 240 mm, is made up of slender uniform rods of mass 1.2 kg/m and the concentrated mass of 3 kg remains at the same position on OC.

Answer   (a) $f_n = 1.903$ Hz (b) $f_n = 1.766$ Hz.

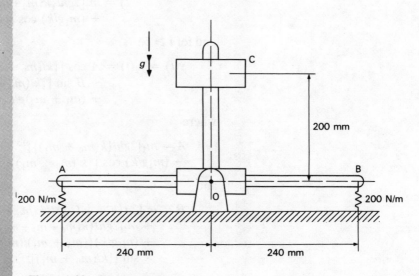

Figure 1.30   Problem 1.6.

1.7 A truck of mass m_0 is loaded from a crane which drops the loads from the same altitude (in relation to the railway track). The stiffness of the truck suspension is k. At time $t = 0$ a load of mass m_1 impacts the truck. After t_0 seconds a second load of mass m_2 impacts the same truck. The loads are released from a height h above a

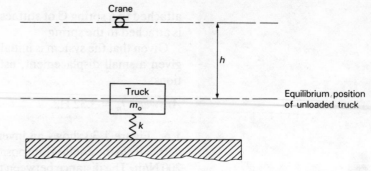

Figure 1.31   Problem 1.7.

reference equilibrium position of the unloaded truck, as shown in Figure 1.31. Impacts are nonelastic.

Obtain expressions for the truck displacement (relative to the equilibrium position of the unloaded truck) for time $0 \leqslant t \leqslant t_0$ and $t \geqslant t_0$.

Assume that the truck with its suspension forms a system with a single degree of freedom and can execute vibrations vertically.

Answer   For $0 \leqslant t \leqslant t_0$:

$$y(t) = m_1[2gh/\{k(m_0 + m_1)\}]^{0.5} \sin[\{k/(m_0 + m_1)\}^{0.5}t] \\ - (m_1 g/k) \cos[\{k/(m_0 + m_1)\}^{0.5}t] + m_1 g/k,$$

and for $t \geqslant t_0$:

$$y(t) = y_2(t) = A \cos[\{k/(m_0 + m_1 + m_2)\}^{0.5}(t - t_0)] \\ + B \sin[\{k/(m_0 + m_1 + m_2)\}^{0.5}(t - t_0)] \\ + (m_1 + m_2)g/k,$$

where

$$A = m_1[2gh/\{k(m_0 + m_1)\}]^{0.5} \sin[\{k/(m_0 + m_1)\}^{0.5}t_0] \\ - (m_1 g/k) \cos[\{k/(m_0 + m_1)\}^{0.5}t_0] - m_2 g/k$$

and

$$B = m_2[2g\{h + y_1(t_0)\}/\{k(m_0 + m_1 + m_2)\}]^{0.5} \\ + m_1[2gh/\{k(m_0 + m_1 + m_2)\}]^{0.5} \cos[\{k/(m_0 + m_1)\}^{0.5}t_0] \\ + (m_1 g/k)\{(m_0 + m_1)/(m_0 + m_1 + m_2)\}^{0.5} \\ \times \sin[\{k/(m_0 + m_1)\}^{0.5}t_0].$$

1.8   Consider the system described in Problem 1.7. Assume that the stiffness of the truck suspension is 395 kN/m and that the truck mass is 9 tonnes. A load of 1000 kg impacts the truck and 5 s later a further load of 500 kg, released by the crane from the same height h of 0.5 m, impacts the truck. See Figure 1.31.

Determine the amplitude of the displacement of the final vibration.

Answer   81.9 mm.

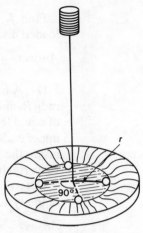

Figure 1.32   Problem 1.9.

1.9   A flywheel is suspended from its centre by a wire hanging from a fixed support. The time period of torsional oscillations of the flywheel about the vertical axis is T_1. Four small, uniformly distributed holes are drilled in the flywheel. See Figure 1.32. The distance of each hole from the flywheel centre line is r and the amount of mass removed for each hole is m. The period of the flywheel's torsional oscillations is now T_2.

Determine the moment of inertia of the flywheel with holes as a function of the measured quantities.

Answer $4mr^2/\{T_1^2/T_2^2 - 1\}$.

1.10   A thin disc is suspended from its centre by a wire which is attached to a fixed support. The mass of the disc amounts to M_0 and its radius is equal to R. The natural frequency of torsional oscillations of the disc about the vertical axis of the wire is f_1. Next many point masses are uniformly attached to the disc at a distance r from its centre, as shown in Figure 1.33. It is known that the mass of the loaded disc is M_1.

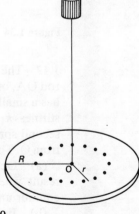

Figure 1.33   Problem 1.10.

Find f_2, the natural frequency of torsional oscillations of the loaded disc, in terms of the stated quantities.

Answer $f_2 = f_1/[1 + \{2r^2(M_1 - M_0)\}/(M_0R^2)]^{0.5}$.

1.11 A hollow cylinder of mass M and with internal and external radii R_1 and R_2, respectively, is suspended by four equi-spaced wires of equal length l. The wires are attached to a fixed support at their upper ends, as shown in Figure 1.34(a). Three thin rods are inserted inside the hollow cylinder in the manner shown in Figure 1.34(b). Each rod has the same length R_1 and mass m.

Determine the natural circular frequency of torsional oscillations of the system.

Answer $\omega_n = (\{R_2^2(M + 3m)g\}/[l\{0.5M(R_1^2 + R_2^2) + mR_1^2\}])^{0.5}$.

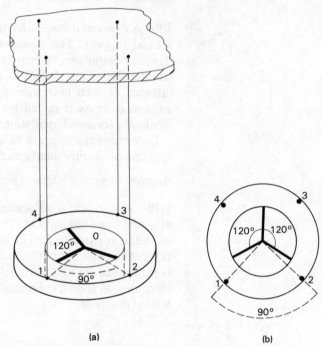

(a)   (b)

Figure 1.34   Problem 1.11.

1.12 The system shown in Figure 1.35 consists of a thin uniform rod OA, of mass m and length l, which is pivoted at the point O and has a small body of mass m_0 fixed to the top of the rod. A spring of stiffness k_1 is attached to the rod at a distance a from the pivot and a second spring of stiffness k_2 is attached to the rod at a distance b from O. The system is initially in equilibrium in the vertical position.

(a)   Determine the natural frequency of the oscillations which result when the system is given a small displacement from its equilibrium position.

(b)   Establish the condition for instability of the system.

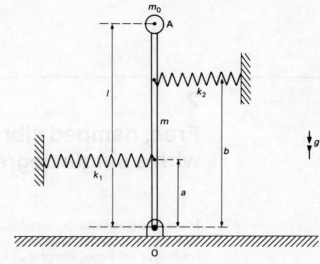

Figure 1.35   Problem 1.12.

Answer

(a) $\{1/(2\pi)\}[(k_1 a^2 + k_2 b^2 - m_0 g l - 0.5 m g l)/\{l^2(m_0 + m/3)\}]^{0.5}$,

(b) $k_1 a^2 + k_2 b^2 < m_0 g l + 0.5 m g l$.

2

Free, damped vibrations of systems with a single degree of freedom

In practice vibrations die away because a damping force acts somewhere on the system. In this chapter we consider the damping to be viscous or equivalent to viscous damping. Viscous damping may be achieved in a dashpot comprising a piston in a cylinder filled with oil, as in Figure 2.1. The piston is pierced by small holes so that laminar flow of oil can occur as the piston moves. The damping force on the piston is proportional to the piston velocity and always opposes the direction of motion of the piston. The schematic representation of the dashpot is also shown in Figure 2.1.

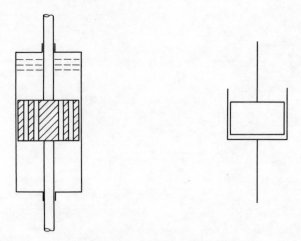

Figure 2.1   Viscous damper and its schematic representation.

In many cases the damping will be provided by rubber supports which also act as the springs. Although for a system with rubber supports the damping force is not as a rule proportional to velocity, proportionality is often assumed and the rubber is regarded as providing equivalent viscous damping.

**Example 2.1
Viscous damping
element in dashpot**

A dashpot consists of a piston of diameter D enclosed in a cylinder through both ends of which the piston rod projects. The cylinder is completely filled with oil of viscosity η which can flow through four small holes of radius r and length l drilled through the piston, which has a mass m.

Assuming that the oil flow through the holes is laminar, show that the displacement of the piston rod under an applied constant force F after t seconds is:

$$(F\tau^2/m)[\exp(-t/\tau) + t/\tau - 1],$$

where $\tau = (8m/\pi\eta l)(r/D)^4$.

Solution As the piston moves in the oil there is a drag or damping force R opposing the motion. There is also a pressure difference of Δp across the holes of the piston. This situation is shown in Figure 2.2, as the piston moves with velocity v.

From Newton's second law the equation of motion is given by

$$F - R = m(dv/dt).$$

The damping force is related to the pressure difference Δp by:

$$R = \Delta p \times \pi D^2/4.$$

As the flow is laminar the Hagen–Poiseuille equation applies, which relates Δp to the flow rate through one hole, q:

$$\Delta p = 8\eta l q/\pi r^4.$$

The oil that flows through the holes is displaced from one side of the piston to the other, so for four holes:

$$4q = (\pi D^2/4)v.$$

We make use of the above equations to eliminate R, Δp and q from the equation of motion.

$$F - (\pi\eta l D^4/8r^4)v = m(dv/dt).$$

Finally,

$$\tau(dv/dt) + v = (\tau/m)F \quad \text{where} \quad \tau = (8m/\pi\eta l)(r/D)^4. \qquad [2.1]$$

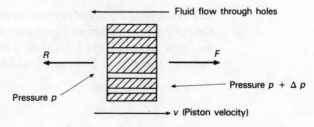

Fluid flow through holes

R F

Pressure $p + \Delta p$

Pressure p

v (Piston velocity)

Figure 2.2   Piston of dashpot.

The general solution of this first-order differential equation comprises a particular integral and a complementary function. As F is a constant the particular integral is also a constant A. Putting $v = A$ in equation [2.1] we obtain $A = (\tau/m)F$.

The complementary function is the general solution of the homogeneous equation: $\tau(dv/dt) + v = 0$. The postulated form of the solution of the homogeneous equation is: $v = B \exp(\lambda t)$. Hence the auxiliary equation for this homogeneous equation is:

$$\tau\lambda + 1 = 0 \qquad \text{and} \qquad \lambda = -1/\tau.$$

Therefore the general solution of the differential equation [2.1] may be written as:

$$v = (\tau/m)F + B \exp(-t/\tau).$$

The constant B is determined from the initial condition: at $t = 0$, $v = 0$. Therefore,

$$0 = (\tau/m)F + B, \qquad \text{hence} \qquad B = -(\tau/m)F$$

and finally

$$v = (\tau/m)F - (\tau/m)F \exp(-t/\tau).$$

To obtain an expression for the displacement x, we have to integrate the above expression. So

$$x = \int v \, dt$$

$$= (\tau/m)Ft + (\tau^2/m)F \exp(-t/\tau) + C.$$

To determine the constant C we use the initial condition: at $t = 0$, $x = 0$. Hence

$$C = -(\tau^2/m)F.$$

Thus

$$x = (F\tau^2/m)[\exp(-t/\tau) + t/\tau - 1],$$

where $\tau = (8m/\pi\eta l)(r/D)^4$.

2.1 The differential equation for free, damped motion

Let us consider a body of mass m supported on a spring and a dashpot. As the body is deflected from the equilibrium position, the free-body diagram becomes that of Figure 2.3. c is the damping constant in N per m/s and the damping force is $c\dot{y}$. The equation of motion is:

$$-ky - c\dot{y} = m\ddot{y},$$

or

$$m\ddot{y} + c\dot{y} + ky = 0. \tag{2.2}$$

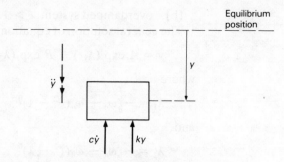

Figure 2.3 Example 2.2. Free-body diagram.

The differential equation [2.2] may be written in the form:

$$\ddot{y} + 2\xi\omega_n\dot{y} + \omega_n^2 y = 0, \tag{2.3}$$

where ξ is called the damping ratio or damping factor and ω_n is the undamped circular natural frequency. The postulated solution of equation [2.3] is in the form $y = A \exp(\lambda t)$, and substitution of this solution in [2.3] leads to a quadratic equation in λ called the auxiliary (or characteristic) equation:

$$\lambda^2 + 2\xi\omega_n\lambda + \omega_n^2 = 0. \tag{2.4}$$

When the roots of the auxiliary equation are equal the damping ratio $\xi = 1$ and a state of the system known as critical damping occurs. The damping constant for critical damping is $2(mk)^{0.5}$.

2.2 Solution of the differential equation

There are three possible solutions of equation [2.3].

(a) underdamped system $\xi < 1$.
In this case the roots of the auxiliary equation [2.4] λ_1 and λ_2 are complex, and

$$\lambda_1 = -\xi\omega_n + i\omega_n(1 - \xi^2)^{0.5},$$
$$\lambda_2 = -\xi\omega_n - i\omega_n(1 - \xi^2)^{0.5},$$

where $i = \sqrt{-1}$. The general solution may be written in the form:

$$y = \exp(-\xi\omega_n t)(A \cos \omega_d t + B \sin \omega_d t), \tag{2.5}$$

where ω_d is the damped circular natural frequency and is related to ω_n by:

$$\omega_d = \omega_n(1 - \xi^2)^{0.5}.$$

An alternative form of the general solution is:

$$y = C \exp(-\xi\omega_n t) \cos(\omega_d t - \Phi). \tag{2.6}$$

Note that there must be two constants, either A and B or C and Φ, which are determined from the initial conditions.

Solutions [2.5] and [2.6] represent a damped sinusoid.

(b)   overdamped system $\xi > 1$.
The general solution of equation [2.3] is written as:

$$y = A \exp(\lambda_1 t) + B \exp(\lambda_2 t), \qquad [2.7]$$

where

$$\lambda_1 = -\xi\omega_n + \omega_n(\xi^2 - 1)^{0.5}$$

and

$$\lambda_2 = -\xi\omega_n - \omega_n(\xi^2 - 1)^{0.5}.$$

The solution for the motion of the overdamped system is non-oscillatory and y tends to zero as t tends to infinity.

(c)   critical damping $\xi = 1$
The general solution of equation [2.3] in the case of repeated roots of equation [2.4] is:

$$y = (A + Bt) \exp(-\omega_n t).$$

Example 2.2
Rectilinear,
spring–mass–damper
system

A body of mass 5.5 kg is hung on a spring of stiffness 1000 N/m. It is pulled down 50 mm below the position of static equilibrium and released so that it executes vertical vibrations. There is a viscous damping force acting on the body of 40 N when the velocity is 1 m/s.
(a)   Determine the differential equation of the motion and obtain the expression for the displacement of the body as a function of time.
(b)   Calculate the distance the body moves from the instant of release until it is momentarily at rest at the highest point of its travel, and the time that has elapsed when it reaches that position.
(c)   Calculate the time that elapses for the body to pass through the equilibrium position for the first time after release.

Solution   (a)   The free-body diagram of Figure 2.3 applies in this problem. Putting numerical values into equation [2.2], we obtain:

$$5.5\ddot{y} + 40\dot{y} + 1000y = 0.$$

Hence

$$\ddot{y} + 7.273\dot{y} + 181.82y = 0.$$

This differential equation should now be compared with the standard form of equation [2.3]. Thus

$$\omega_n = (181.82)^{0.5} = 13.484 \text{ rad/s},$$
$$\xi = 7.273/(2 \times 13.484) = 0.2697.$$

$\xi < 1$, so the system is underdamped, thus

$$\omega_d = \omega_n(1 - \xi^2)^{0.5} = 12.984.$$

Substituting the value of ω_d in equation [2.5], we obtain:

$$y = \exp(-3.6366t)(A \cos 12.984t + B \sin 12.984t). \qquad [2.8]$$

We need two initial conditions to determine the constants A and B. Firstly, when $t = 0$, $y = 50 \times 10^{-3}$ m. Hence

$$50 \times 10^{-3} = \exp(-3.6366 \times 0)(A \cos 0 + B \sin 0) = A.$$

Secondly, when $t = 0$, $\dot{y} = 0$.

Next, we have to differentiate equation [2.8]:

$$\dot{y} = \exp(-3.6366t)(-12.984A \sin 12.984t + 12.984B \cos 12.984t)$$
$$- 3.6366 \exp(-3.6366t)(A \cos 12.984t + B \sin 12.984t).$$
$$[2.9]$$

Thus

$$0 = 12.984B - 3.6366A.$$

And

$$B = 3.6366 \times 50 \times 10^{-3}/12.984 = 14.0 \times 10^{-3} \text{ m} \quad \text{(or 14.0 mm)}.$$

The solution of the above differential equation for damped motion is:

$$y = \exp(-3.6366t)(50 \cos 12.984t + 14.0 \sin 12.984t) \text{ mm}.$$
$$[2.10]$$

(b)   A sketch of the displacement against time is shown in Figure 2.4. We have to find the time and displacement at point Q. At Q $\dot{y} = 0$.

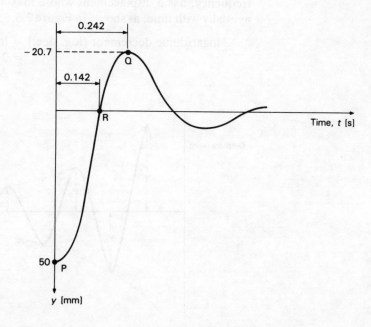

Figure 2.4   Example 2.2. Sketch of displacement against time.

Substituting the values of A and B into equation [2.9] we can show that:

$$\dot{y} = \exp(-3.6366t)(-0.700112 \sin 12.984t) \text{ m/s}.$$

When $\dot{y} = 0$, $\sin 12.984t = 0$ and $12.984t = 0$, π, 2π, etc. Hence $t = 0$, 0.24195, 0.48390 seconds, etc. $t = 0$ corresponds to P and $t = 0.24195$ s to Q. Putting the value of $t = 0.24195$ s into equation [2.10] gives:

$$y = -20.741 \times 10^{-3} \text{ m}.$$

Hence total distance moved by the body is $50.0 + 20.7 = 70.7$ mm during time of 0.242 s.

(c) The value of time corresponding to point R in Figure 2.4 is required. At point R, $y = 0$. From equation [2.10] one obtains:

$$50.0 \cos 12.984t + 14.0 \sin 12.984t = 0.$$

Therefore,

$$\tan 12.984t = -50.0/14.0 = -3.5714.$$

The angles whose tangent is -3.5714 are $180 - 74.36$, $360 - 74.36$ degrees, etc. For point R the angle required is $105.64°$, and the time elapsed is:

$$105.64(\pi/180)/12.984 = 0.142 \text{ s}.$$

2.3 Logarithmic decrement

A useful way of defining the damping in lightly damped systems is by the logarithmic decrement. A viscously damped system, vibrating at one frequency, has a displacement whose maxima and minima decay exponentially with time, as shown in Figure 2.5.

$$\begin{aligned}
\text{logarithmic decrement (log. dec.)} &= \ln(Y_1/Y_2) \\
&= 2\pi\xi/(1 - \xi^2)^{0.5} \\
&= 2\pi\xi, \text{ for small values of } \xi.
\end{aligned}$$

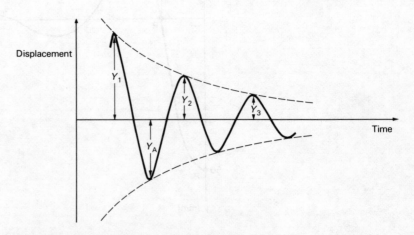

Figure 2.5   Decay of displacement with time.

In many cases Y_1 and Y_2 can be measured even though the exact shape of the curve cannot be obtained. Theoretically the same value of logarithmic decrement should be obtained from Y_2 and Y_3 as from Y_1 and Y_2, although in an experiment there may be some difference.

If only Y_1 and Y_A are known then:

$$\ln (Y_1/Y_A) = \pi\xi/(1 - \xi^2)^{0.5}.$$

Example 2.3
Damping in terms of
logarithmic decrement

The disc of a torsional pendulum has a moment of inertia of 0.6 kg m² and is immersed in a viscous fluid. The disc is suspended on a brass shaft which has a diameter of 9.0 mm and length of 400 mm. When the pendulum is oscillating the amplitudes that are observed on the same side of the mid-position for three successive cycles are 14.4°, 1.2° and 0.1°.

Take modulus of rigidity G to be 34.5 GN/m² for brass.

Determine:
(a) the logarithmic decrement,
(b) the damping ratio,
(c) the undamped circular natural frequency,
(d) the damped circular natural frequency,
(e) the damping torque at unit angular velocity.

Solution (a) A sketch of the decaying oscillation is shown in Figure 2.6.

$$\text{log. dec.} = \ln (14.4/1.2) = 2.485 \quad (\text{or } \ln 1.2/0.1).$$

(b) log. dec. $= 2\pi\xi/(1 - \xi^2)^{0.5}$.

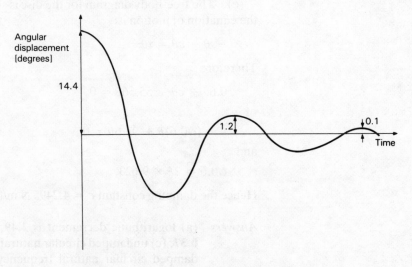

Figure 2.6   Example 2.3. Sketch of decaying oscillation.

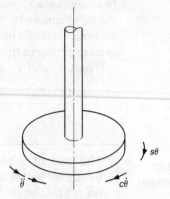

Figure 2.7   Example 2.3. Free-body diagram for the disc.

Therefore:

$$2.485^2(1 - \xi^2) = 4\pi^2\xi^2.$$

Hence,

$$\text{damping ratio } \xi = 0.368.$$

(c)   torsional stiffness of the shaft: $s = GI_p/l$.
$s = 34.5 \times 10^9\{\pi(9.0 \times 10^{-3})^4/32\}/0.4 = 55.56 \text{ N m/rad}$.
$\omega_n^2 = s/I = 55.56/0.6 = 92.6$.

Hence undamped circular natural frequency ω_n is 9.623 rad/s.

(d)   The damped circular natural frequency is given by:

$$\omega_d = \omega_n(1 - \xi^2)^{0.5} = 8.948 \text{ rad/s}.$$

(e)   The free-body diagram for the disc is shown in Figure 2.7. Hence the equation of motion is:

$$-s\theta - c\dot{\theta} = I\ddot{\theta}.$$

Therefore

$$0.6\ddot{\theta} + c\dot{\theta} + 55.56\theta = 0$$

or

$$\ddot{\theta} + (c/0.6)\dot{\theta} + 92.6\theta = 0$$

and

$$c/0.6 = 2\xi \times 9.623.$$

Hence the damping constant $c = 4.2495 \text{ N m/(rad/s)}$.

Answers   (a) logarithmic decrement is **2.49**, (b) the damping ratio is **0.37**, (c) undamped circular natural frequency is **9.6 rad/s**, (d) damped circular natural frequency is **8.9 rad/s** and (e) the damping constant is **4.2 N m s/rad**.

Example 2.4
Experimental determination of damping ratio

In an experiment to measure the damping ratio of a system with a single degree of freedom a solid disc is suspended from a fixed support by a thin steel wire. In the first part of the experiment the disc is allowed to perform torsional oscillations freely in air. Five sets of ten oscillations, which were measured by a stop watch, took 60.4, 60.5, 60.3, 60.5 and 60.5 s.

In the second part of the test the disc was immersed in a bowl of a light oil, as shown in Figure 2.8. During the damped vibration it was possible to time six oscillations. This was done on four separate occasions, and the times for the six oscillations were 36.5, 36.2, 36.6 and 36.4 s. The disc carried a pointer which moved over a fixed scale as the disc oscillated. In the equilibrium position the pointer coincided with the zero of the scale. The disc and pointer were rotated about the wire axis by a known angle and released. The angles on the scale corresponding to the maxima and minima were observed visually during the subsequent oscillations. The results are shown in Table 2.1.

Table 2.1

Time (no. of periods)	0	0.5	1	1.5	2	2.5	3	3.5	4	4.5	5	5.5	6
Maxima (degrees)	118.8		62.6		34.6		19.3		10.8		5.8		3.3
Minima (degrees)		91.0		47.5		25.2		13.7		8.2		4.1	

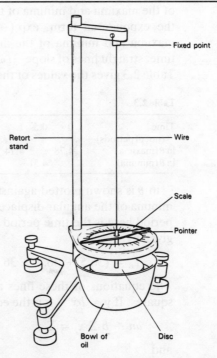

Fixed point

Retort stand

Wire

Scale

Pointer

Bowl of oil

Disc

Figure 2.8 Apparatus for determination of damping ratio.

In the third part of the test the disc was immersed in a heavy oil. When the disc was displaced and released the resulting motion was non-oscillatory. During the motion the times corresponding to certain angles were recorded, and are shown in Table 2.2.

Table 2.2

Time (seconds)	0	2.6	3.78	4.95	6.3	8.15	10.8
Angular position (degrees)	122.5	62.5	42.5	32.5	22.5	12.5	7.5

Estimate the damping ratios for the system with (a) the light oil and (b) the heavy oil.

Solution The oscillations in free air for the first part of the experiment can be regarded as undamped, and hence can be used to determine the undamped natural frequency. The average time for ten oscillations is 60.44 s. Therefore time period is 6.044 s and the undamped circular natural frequency is $2\pi/6.044 = 1.040$ rad/s.

(a) Light oil

The expression for the angular displacement θ during this under-damped oscillation is:

$$\theta = \exp(-\xi\omega_n t)\theta_0 \cos(\omega_d t - \Phi),$$

where θ_0 is the amplitude at $t = 0$ (in this case 118.8°) and Φ is a phase angle. The above equation is the equivalent of equation [2.6]. The decay of the maxima and minima of the angular displacements is controlled by the exponential term, $\exp(-\xi\omega_n t)$. If the natural logarithms of the maxima and minima of the angular displacements are plotted against time, straight lines of slope $-\xi\omega_n$ should be obtained for viscous damping. Table 2.3 gives the values of these logarithms.

Table 2.3

Time (no. pf periods)	0	0.5	1	1.5	2	2.5	3	3.5	4	4.5	5	5.5	6
ln θ (maxima)	4.78		4.14		3.54		2.96		2.38		1.76		1.19
ln θ (minima)		4.51		3.86		3.23		2.62		2.1		1.41	

ln θ is shown plotted against number of time periods for maxima and minima of the angular displacement in Figure 2.9. The appropriate time period here is the time period of the damped oscillation T_d, where T_d is given by:

$$T_d = (36.5 + 36.2 + 36.6 + 36.4)/(4 \times 6) = 6.071 \text{ s}.$$

The equations of these lines are best obtained by the method of least squares. If $y = bx + a$ is the equation of a straight line, then

$$an + b \sum x_j = \sum y_j$$

and

$$a \sum x_j + b \sum x_j^2 = \sum x_j y_j,$$

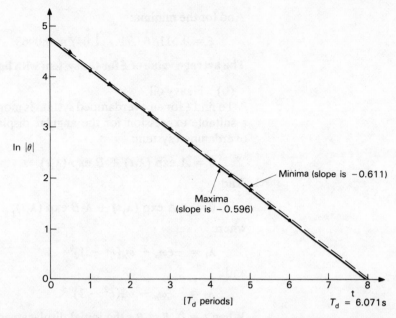

Figure 2.9   Natural logarithms of maxima and minima of angular displacements plotted against time periods for underdamped system (light oil).

where $\Sigma\ x_j$ and $\Sigma\ y_j$ represent the sums of the x and y co-ordinates of the points, respectively. In this example ln θ for maxima and minima form the y co-ordinates and the number of periods the x co-ordinates. For the line representing the maxima of angular displacement:

$$7a + 21b = 20.75,$$
$$21a + 91b = 45.56.$$

Hence $a = 4.752$ and $b = -0.596$. Thus the equation of the line is:

$$y = -0.596x + 4.752.$$

For the line representing the minima:

$$6a + 18b = 17.73,$$
$$18a + 71.50b = 42.495.$$

Hence $a = 4.788$ and $b = -0.611$. Thus the equation of the line is:

$$y = -0.611x + 4.788.$$

Remembering that x is in terms of damped time periods (where $T_d = 6.071$ s) we may write for the maxima:

$$\xi\omega_n = 0.596/6.071.$$

Thus

$$\xi = 0.596/(6.071 \times 1.04) = 0.0944.$$

And for the minima:

$$\xi = 0.611/(6.071 \times 1.04) = 0.0968.$$

The average value of ξ for the system with light oil is 0.096.

(b)   Heavy oil

To find ξ for an overdamped system is more difficult. We must first find a suitable expression for the angular displacement. In general, for an overdamped system:

$$\theta = A \exp (\lambda_1 t) + B \exp (\lambda_2 t).$$

And

$$\dot{\theta} = \lambda_1 A \exp (\lambda_1 t) + \lambda_2 B \exp (\lambda_2 t),$$

where

$$\lambda_1 = -\xi \omega_n + \omega_n (\xi^2 - 1)^{0.5}$$

and

$$\lambda_2 = -\xi \omega_n - \omega_n (\xi^2 - 1)^{0.5}.$$

When $t = 0$, $\theta = \theta_0$, the initial displacement. Thus $\theta_0 = A + B$. When $t = 0$, $\dot{\theta} = 0$, as the disc is initially at rest. So $0 = \lambda_1 A + \lambda_2 B$. Hence

$$A = \theta_0 [\xi + (\xi^2 - 1)^{0.5}]/[2(\xi^2 - 1)^{0.5}]$$

and

$$B = \theta_0 [-\xi + (\xi^2 - 1)^{0.5}]/[2(\xi^2 - 1)^{0.5}].$$

Of these two constants A is the larger and has the larger absolute value. Also λ_2 of negative value has a larger absolute value compared with λ_1, so $\exp (\lambda_2 t)$ decays more quickly with time than $\exp (\lambda_1 t)$. Thus,

$$A \exp (\lambda_1 t) \gg B \exp (\lambda_2 t).$$

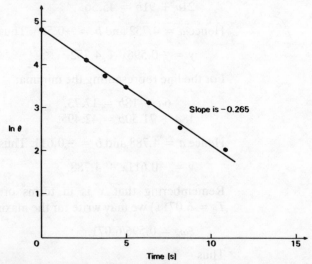

Figure 2.10   Natural logarithms of angular displacement plotted against time for overdamped system (heavy oil).

Therefore as an approximation for the angular displacement we may write: $\theta = A \exp(\lambda_1 t)$. Thus in a graph of ln θ against time the slope is equal to λ_1. This graph has been constructed in Figure 2.10.

We use the method of least squares again to obtain the best fitted straight line. The y co-ordinates are the natural logarithms of the angular displacements (Table 2.2). $n = 7$, $\Sigma x_j = 36.58$, $\Sigma y_j = 23.83$, $\Sigma x_j^2 = 268.3$, $\Sigma x_j y_j = 104.122$. Hence

$$7a + 36.58b = 23.83 \quad \text{and} \quad 36.58a + 268.3b = 104.122.$$

Thus $a = 4.79$ and $b = -0.265$, hence $y = -0.265x + 4.79$. The slope of the straight line (-0.265) is equal to λ_1, hence

$$-\xi\omega_n + \omega_n(\xi^2 - 1)^{0.5} = -0.265 \quad \text{and} \quad \xi = 2.09.$$

The damping ratio of the system with heavy oil is 2.1.

Example 2.5
Damped vibration with different system equilibrium positions

A schematic diagram of a balance for weighing purposes is shown in Figure 2.11. The beam and scale pans form a rigid body which has a moment of inertia of 0.01 kg m² about the rotation axis through the pivot point O. Springs and viscous dampers are shown. Determine the undamped natural frequency and the damping ratio of the system when it undergoes oscillations of small amplitude.

If a mass of 5 kg is gently placed in contact with, for example, the right-hand scale pan and released, find the maximum deflection of the beam.

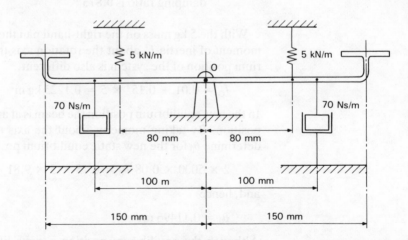

Figure 2.11 Example 2.5. Schematic diagram of balance.

Solution For the case in which the beam is deflected clockwise through an angle θ the forces, relative to those at static equilibrium, are shown in the free-body diagram of Figure 2.12. Let us take moments about

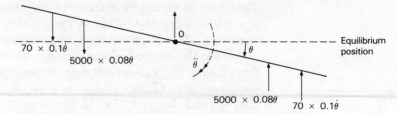

Figure 2.12   Example 2.5. Free-body diagram for the beam.

the fixed axis through O and write down the equation of motion for the beam:

$$\Sigma M_O = I_O \ddot{\theta}.$$

or

$$-2 \times 5000 \times 0.08^2\theta - 2 \times 70 \times 0.1^2\dot{\theta} = 0.01\ddot{\theta}.$$

Hence,

$$\ddot{\theta} + 140\dot{\theta} + 6400\theta = 0.$$

Thus

$$\omega_n = 6400^{0.5} = 80 \text{ rad/s} \quad \text{and} \quad 2\xi\omega_n = 140,$$

so $\xi = 0.875.$

Answer   The undamped circular natural frequency is **80 rad/s** and the damping ratio is **0.875**.

   With the 5 kg mass on the right-hand pan the rigid body has now a new moment of inertia I_O' about the rotation axis through O and the equilibrium position of the system is also different.

$$I_O' = 0.01 + 0.15^2 \times 5 = 0.1225 \text{ kg m}^2.$$

In the new equilibrium position the beam is at an angle θ_0 to the horizontal position. By taking moments about the axis through O we are able to determine θ_0 for the new static equilibrium position:

$$2 \times 5000 \times 0.08^2\theta_0 = 0.15 \times 5 \times 9.81$$

and, hence

$$\theta_0 = 0.11496 \text{ rad}.$$

Although the equilibrium position is now different from the previous equilibrium position we will retain the previously defined variable θ. This means that the forces shown in the free-body diagram of Figure 2.12 are not relative to the new equilibrium position. When we analyse moments about the rotational axis through O we must now consider an additional clockwise moment, due to the 5 kg mass on the pan, of $5 \times 9.81 \times 0.15$ N m. Hence:

$$-2 \times 5000 \times 0.08^2\theta - 2 \times 70 \times 0.1^2\dot{\theta} + 5 \times 9.81 \times 0.15$$
$$= 0.1225\ddot{\theta}.$$

And

$$\ddot{\theta} + 11.429\dot{\theta} + 522.45\theta = 60.06. \tag{2.11}$$

Thus

$$\omega_n = 22.86 \text{ rad/s} \quad \text{and} \quad \xi = 0.250.$$

The damped natural circular frequency $\omega_d = \omega_n(1 - \xi^2)^{0.5} = 22.13$ rad/s.

The general solution of the differential equation [2.11] comprises a particular integral θ_{PI} and a complementary function θ_{CF}. As the right-hand side of equation [2.11] is a constant, it is clear that the particular integral will also be a constant. Hence $\dot{\theta}_{PI}$ and $\ddot{\theta}_{PI}$ are equal to zero, so

$$522.45\theta_{PI} = 60.06 \quad \text{and hence} \quad \theta_{PI} = 0.11496 \text{ rad.}$$

This value is the same as θ_0, the displacement of the equilibrium position of the system. An expression for the complementary function has been obtained before (equation [2.5]).

$$\theta_{CF} = \exp\left(-\xi\omega_n t\right)\{A \cos \omega_d t + B \sin \omega_d t\}$$

or

$$\theta_{CF} = \exp\left(-5.715t\right)\{A \cos 22.13t + B \sin 22.13t\}.$$

The general solution for θ is given by:

$$\theta = 0.11496 + \exp\left(-5.715t\right)\{A \cos 22.13t + B \sin 22.13t\}.$$

To find A and B we require the initial conditions. The 5 kg mass is gently placed on the scale pan and released. $t = 0$ is the moment when the 5 kg mass is released. The beam then rotates clockwise away from the original equilibrium position and after a damped oscillation settles down to the new equilibrium position. Thus when $t = 0$, $\theta = 0$, and substituting this condition into the general solution gives:

$$0 = 0.11496 + A \quad \text{and hence} \quad A = -0.11496.$$

At the moment of release of the 5 kg mass the balance is at rest, so at $t = 0$, $\dot{\theta} = 0$.

$$\dot{\theta} = -5.715 \exp\left(-5.715t\right)\{A \cos 22.13t + B \sin 22.13t\}$$
$$+ \exp\left(-5.715t\right)\{-22.13A \sin 22.13t + 22.13B \cos 22.13t\},$$
$$\dot{\theta} = \exp\left(-5.715t\right)\{(2.544 - 5.715B) \sin 22.13t$$
$$+ (0.6570 + 22.13B) \cos 22.13t\}.$$

Thus

$$0 = 0.6570 + 22.13B \quad \text{and hence} \quad B = -0.02969.$$

We now have the solution for θ. To find the maximum deflection of the scale pan we must find out when the pan is first momentarily at rest after its motion has started. We probably are aware that this will occur after half a period, but let us confirm this. For the beam at rest $\dot{\theta} = 0$.

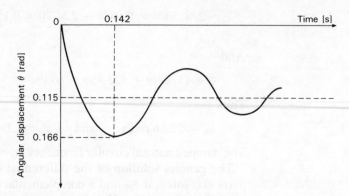

Figure 2.13   Example 2.5. Sketch of angular displacement against time.

$$\dot{\theta} = \exp(-5.715t) \times 2.7137 \sin 22.13t$$

(coefficient of cos term is 0).

Thus $\sin 21.13t = 0$ or $22.13t = 0, \pi, 2\pi$, etc. We require $22.13t = \pi$ or $t = \pi/22.13 = 0.14196$ s. Substituting this value of t in the solution for θ gives the value:

$$0.11496 + 0.4443\{-0.11496 \cos(22.13 \times 0.14196)$$
$$-0.02969 \sin(22.13 \times 0.14196)\}$$
$$= 0.11496 + 0.4443 \times 0.11496 = 0.1660 \text{ rad } (9.51°).$$

A sketch of how θ varies with time is shown in Figure 2.13.

Answer   The maximum angle through which the beam swings is **9.5°**.

Example 2.6
Rotor oscillation induced by a sudden impulse

The rotor of an indicating instrument is controlled by a torsional spring and viscous damper. The rotor has a mass of 50 g and its radius of gyration about the axis of rotation is 12 mm. When set in vibration the rotor makes one complete oscillation in 4.2 s and the amplitudes of consecutive swings, in opposite directions, are 90 : 12.

(a)   Determine:
(1)   the damping ratio,
(2)   the undamped natural frequency,
(3)   the stiffness of the torsional spring,
(4)   the damping constant of the viscous damper.

(b)   If the rotor, initially at rest, receives a sudden impulse, which causes it to swing through an angle of 25°, determine:
(1)   the time taken to swing through 25°,
(2)   the initial angular velocity caused by the impulse,
(3)   the energy supplied by the impulse.

Solution   (a)   (1)   When set in vibration the rotor makes one complete oscillation, the ratio of the amplitudes of consecutive swings in opposite directions is 90/12. Thus,

$$\ln (90/12) = \pi \xi/(1 - \xi^2)^{0.5} \text{ or}$$
$$0.411347 = \xi^2/(1 - \xi^2) \quad \text{and} \quad \xi = 0.5399.$$

The damping ratio is 0.54.

(a)   (2)   The time period for one damped oscillation is 4.2 s. Thus

$$\omega_d = 2\pi/4.2 = 1.4960 \text{ rad/s.}$$

The undamped circular natural frequency is given by:

$$\omega_n = \omega_d/(1 - \xi^2)^{0.5}.$$

Hence

$$\omega_n = 1.496/(1 - 0.5399^2)^{0.5} = 1.7773 \text{ rad/s.}$$

And

$$f_n = 0.2829 \text{ Hz.}$$

The undamped natural frequency is 0.283 Hz.

(a)   (3)   If c is the damping constant of the viscous damper, s is the torsional stiffness of the spring and I is the moment of inertia of the rotor, the differential equation describing the motion of the system is:

$$I\ddot{\theta} + c\dot{\theta} + s\theta = 0$$

or

$$\ddot{\theta} + (c/I)\dot{\theta} + (s/I)\theta = 0. \tag{2.12}$$

The standard form (equation [2.3]) is $\ddot{\theta} + 2\xi\omega_n\dot{\theta} + \omega_n^2\theta = 0$; hence

$$\omega_n^2 = s/I \quad \text{and} \quad s = 1.7773^2 \times 50 \times 10^{-3}(12 \times 10^{-3})^2$$

or

$$s = 22.743 \times 10^{-6} \text{ N m/rad.}$$

The torsional stiffness of the spring is 22.7×10^{-6} N m/rad.

(a)   (4)   We know that $2\xi\omega_n = c/I$.

Thus

$$c = 2 \times 0.5399 \times 1.7773 \times 50 \times 10^{-3}(12 \times 10^{-3})^2,$$
$$c = 13.818 \times 10^{-6} \text{ N m/(rad/s).}$$

Damping constant of the viscous damper is 13.8×10^{-6} N m/(rad/s).

(b)   (1) and (2)   The form of the general solution of differential equation [2.12] is the same as the form of expression in equation [2.5]. Hence

$$\theta = \exp (-\xi\omega_n t)(A \cos \omega_d t + B \sin \omega_d t).$$

Substituting numerical values for ξ, ω_n and ω_d, we obtain:

$$\theta = \exp(-0.95956t)(A \cos 1.496t + B \sin 1.496t). \qquad [2.13]$$

An expression for the velocity is:

$$\dot{\theta} = \exp(-0.95956t)(-1.496A \sin 1.496t + 1.496B \cos 1.496t)$$
$$- 0.95956 \exp(-0.95956t)(A \cos 1.496t + B \sin 1.496t). \qquad [2.14]$$

To determine the constants A and B in equations [2.13] and [2.14] the initial conditions are required. Namely, when $t = 0$: $\theta = 0$ and $\dot{\theta} = \Omega$, where Ω is an initial angular velocity, so far unknown, which results from the application of the impulse. From these initial conditions we obtain:

$$A = 0, \qquad \Omega = 1.496B. \qquad [2.15]$$

Let T_s denote the time during which the rotor swings through 25° (i.e., $25\pi/180$ radians). It should be noted that $\dot{\theta}(T_s) = 0$. Therefore, from equations [2.13] and [2.14] one obtains:

$$25\pi/180 = \exp(-0.95956T_s)(B \sin 1.496T_s), \qquad [2.16]$$
$$0 = \exp(-0.95956T_s)(1.496B \cos 1.496T_s$$
$$- 0.95956B \sin 1.496T_s). \qquad [2.17]$$

From equation [2.17], we have: $\tan 1.496T_s = 1.496/0.95956$.
Therefore, $1.496T_s = 1.000$ rad.
$$T_s = 0.6684 \text{ s}.$$
From equation [2.16]: $B = 0.98478$.
From equation [2.15]: $\Omega = 1.4732$ rad/s.
Thus the impulse gives the rotor an angular velocity of 1.47 rad/s and causes the rotor to swing through an angle of 25° in 0.668 s. (You should note that this time of 0.668 s is not a quarter of the time period of 4.2 s.)

(b) (3) The impulse supplies kinetic energy to the rotor of magnitude $0.5 I\Omega^2$. Thus energy supplied

$$= 0.5 \times 50 \times 10^{-3}(12^2 \times 10^{-6})1.4732^2 = 7.813 \ \mu\text{J}.$$

Answers (a) (1) Damping ratio is **0.54,**
                (2) the undamped natural frequency is **0.283 Hz,**
                (3) the stiffness of the spring is **22.7 × 10^{-6} N m/rad,**
                (4) the damping constant is **13.8 × 10^{-6} N s/rad.**
       (b) (1) The time taken to swing through 25° is **0.668 s,**
                (2) the initial angular velocity is **1.47 rad/s,**
                (3) the energy supplied by the impulse is **7.8 μJ.**

**Example 2.7
Problem involving
particular integral**

A heavy-duty weighing machine consists of a platform of mass 800 kg which is supported by springs with an equivalent stiffness of 100 kN/m and a damper which provides viscous damping of damping constant 500 N s/m.

A sand bag of mass 70 kg is dropped from a height of 400 mm and strikes the platform without splitting. Determine the time required for the platform and bag to reach their lowest position during the subsequent vibration. Sketch the displacement of the platform against time.

Solution   The bag strikes the platform with a velocity $(2 \times 9.81 \times 0.4)^{0.5}$. As momentum is conserved the common downwards velocity v of the platform and bag after the inelastic impact can be determined from:

$$870v = 70(2 \times 9.81 \times 0.4)^{0.5}.$$

Hence,

$$v = 0.2254 \text{ m/s}.$$

With the bag on the platform there is a new equilibrium position at a lower level than the previous one. Let us use a variable y measured from the initial equilibrium position. The free-body diagram for the platform and sand bag, showing the forces acting on the body during the vibration, is shown in Figure 2.14. Because the variable y, describing the position of the body (platform and sand bag), is measured from the initial equilibrium position, the weight of the sand bag must be included in the free-body diagram and in the equation of motion. This equation is:

$$-100 \times 10^3 y - 500\dot{y} + 70 \times 9.81 = 870\ddot{y}$$

or

$$\ddot{y} + 0.5747\dot{y} + 114.94y = 0.7893. \qquad [2.18]$$

Thus

$$\omega_n = 114.94^{0.5} = 10.721 \text{ rad/s}.$$

And

$$2\xi\omega_n = 0.5747, \quad \text{so} \quad \xi = 0.0268.$$

The damped circular natural frequency ω_d is given by:

$$\omega_d = 10.721(1 - 0.0268^2)^{0.5} = 10.717.$$

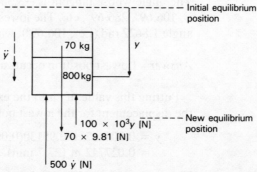

Figure 2.14   Example 2.7. Free-body diagram for platform and bag.

The solution of the differential equation [2.18] comprises a particular integral y_{PI} and a complementary function y_{CF}. As the right-hand side of equation [2.18] is a constant the particular integral must also be a constant. Hence,

$$114.94y_{PI} = 0.7893 \quad \text{and} \quad y_{PI} = 6.867 \times 10^{-3}.$$

Thus the general solution of equation [2.18] may be expressed as:

$$y = 6.867 \times 10^{-3}$$
$$+ \exp(-0.28735t)(A \cos 10.717t + B \sin 10.717t).$$

First initial condition (when $t = 0$) is $y = 0$; hence

$$0 = 6.867 \times 10^{-3} + A \quad \text{and so} \quad A = -0.006867.$$

Second initial condition (when $t = 0$) is $\dot{y} = 0.2254$ m/s.

$$\dot{y} = -0.28735 \exp(-0.28735t)(A \cos 10.717t + B \sin 10.717t)$$
$$+ \exp(-0.28735t)(-10.717A \sin 10.717t$$
$$+ 10.717B \cos 10.717t).$$

Hence,

$$0.2254 = -0.28735A + 10.717B$$

and therefore

$$B = (0.2254 - 0.28735 \times 0.006867)/10.717 = 0.02085.$$

Thus y and $\dot{y}$ are:

$$y = 0.006867 + \exp(-0.28735t)(-0.006867 \cos 10.717t$$
$$+ 0.02085 \sin 10.717t),$$
$$\dot{y} = \exp(-0.28735t)(0.2254 \cos 10.717t + 0.0676 \sin 10.717t).$$

At the lowest position of the body (platform and bag) $\dot{y} = 0$; hence:

$$0.2254 \cos 10.717t + 0.0676 \sin 10.717t = 0.$$

And

$$\tan 10.717t = -3.3343.$$

The angle whose tangent is -3.3343 is 1.8622 rad, 5.0038 rad, etc. That is, 106.69°, 286.69°, etc. The lowest position of the platform refers to the angle 1.8622 rad (i.e., 106.69°), which leads to $t = 0.17376$ s.

Answer Lowest position occurs after **0.174 s.**

Putting this value of t into the expression for y, we obtain the value of the displacement for the lowest position of the platform:

$$y = 0.006867 + 0.95130(0.0019728 + 0.019971)$$
$$= 0.027742 \text{ m (27.7 mm)}.$$

The displacement of the platform against time is sketched in Figure 2.15.

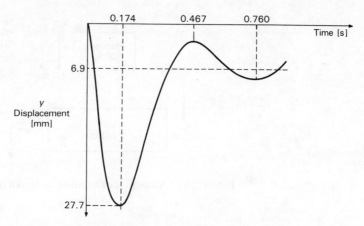

Figure 2.15 Example 2.7. Sketch of displacement against time.

Example 2.8
Initial conditions determined from momentum equation

The anvil of a drop forge has a mass of 2000 kg and rests on supports that have an equivalent combined stiffness of 9.80 MN/m and an equivalent viscous damping constant of 28 kN s/m. The hammer of mass 500 kg falls 1.2 m from rest onto the anvil as shown in Figure 2.16. The coeffiicient of restitution is known to be 0.35.

Determine:

(a) the initial velocity of the anvil after impact,
(b) the maximum downward displacement of the anvil.

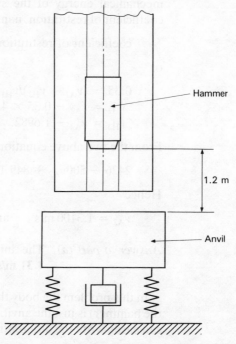

Figure 2.16 Example 2.8. Sketch of hammer and anvil of a drop forge.

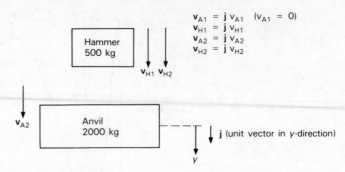

Figure 2.17   Velocities of hammer and anvil before and after impact.

Solution   The velocity of the hammer $\mathbf{v}_{H1}$, just before impact with the anvil, is given by formula:

$$\mathbf{v}_{H1} = \mathbf{j}v_{H1}, \quad v_{H1} = (2 \times 9.81 \times 1.2)^{0.5} = 4.852 \text{ m/s},$$

where $\mathbf{j}$ is a unit vector defined as shown in Figure 2.17. Let the velocities of the hammer and anvil just after impact in relation to the ground be $\mathbf{v}_{H2}$ and $\mathbf{v}_{A2}$, respectively. (Figure 2.17.) By applying the equation for the conservation of momentum for the system (hammer and anvil), we obtain:

$$500(4.852 - v_{H2}) = 2000(v_{A2} - 0).$$ [2.19]

The impact in the considered case is not perfectly elastic and the loss of mechanical energy of the system is taken into account by using the coefficient of restitution, namely:

$$\text{coefficient of restitution} = -(v_{A2} - v_{H2})/(v_{A1} - v_{H1})$$

or

$$0.35 = (v_{A2} - v_{H2})/v_{H1}.$$ [2.20]
$$v_{H2} = v_{A2} - 0.35 \times 4.852.$$
$$v_{H2} = v_{A2} - 1.6982.$$

From the two above equations [2.19, 2.20] we obtain:

$$2426 - 500v_{A2} + 849.1 = 2000v_{A2}.$$

Hence

$$v_{A2} = 1.3100 \text{ m/s} \quad \text{and} \quad v_{H2} = -0.38816 \text{ m/s}.$$

Answer to part (a)   The initial velocity of the anvil after impact is **1.31 m/s.**

In this problem the body that is vibrating after impact (and rebound of the hammer) is just the anvil. Without drawing the free-body diagram we can easily write the differential equation of motion, which is:

$$2000\ddot{y} + 28\,000\dot{y} + 9.8 \times 10^6 y = 0$$

or

$$2\ddot{y} + 28\dot{y} + 9800y = 0,$$

where y is the displacement of the anvil, measured downwards from the equilibrium position of the anvil. Hence

$$\ddot{y} + 14\dot{y} + 4900y = 0.$$

Hence $\omega_n = 4900^{0.5} = 70$ rad/s and $T_n = 0.0898$ s. $2\xi\omega_n = 14$ and $\xi = 0.1$. Also $\omega_d = 69.65$ rad/s and $T_d = 0.0902$ s. The general solution for y may be written in the form:

$$y = \exp(-7t)(A\cos 69.65t + B\sin 69.65t).$$

First initial condition ($t = 0$) is $y = 0$; hence $A = 0$. Second initial condition ($t = 0$) is $\dot{y} = v_{A2} = 1.310$ m/s. Thus

$$1.310 = 69.65B \quad \text{and so} \quad B = 0.0188.$$

Hence

$$y = \exp(-7t)0.0188\sin 69.65t.$$

To obtain the maximum downwards displacement of the anvil we need the value of time for which $\dot{y} = 0$ for the first occasion.

$$0 = 0.0188\exp(-7t)(69.65\cos 69.65t - 7\sin 69.65t).$$

This leads to $\tan 69.65t = 9.95$. Therefore, $69.65t = 1.4706$. This angle of 1.4706 rad is the same as 84.26° and it is the lowest positive value of the angle for which the tangent function is equal to 9.95. The time corresponding to this angle is 0.0211 s and this is the time, measured after impact, which refers to the maximum downward displacement reached by the anvil.

$$y_{max} = \exp(-7 \times 0.0211) \times 0.0188 \times \sin(69.65 \times 0.0211).$$

Hence

$$y_{max} = 0.8627 \times 0.995 \times 0.0188 = 0.016135 \text{ m} \quad \text{(or 16.1 mm)}.$$

Answer to part (b) Maximum downward displacement of the anvil is **16.1 mm.**

**Example 2.9
Damped system with
pre-compression**

A hydraulic buffer consists of two units each having an internal spring of stiffness 30 000 N/m in parallel with a viscous damper offering a resistance to motion of 120 000 N at 1 m/s velocity. The springs are initially pre-compressed an amount 0.3 m. If a train of mass 100 000 kg, moving at a velocity of 2 m/s, strikes the buffer without rebound, determine the distance the train moves before coming momentarily to rest.

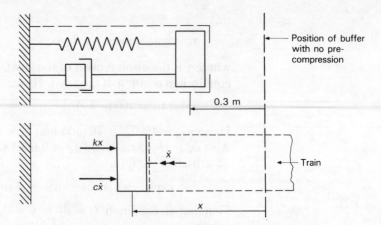

Figure 2.18   Example 2.9. Free-body diagram for buffer and train.

Solution   In the equilibrium position the springs are compressed by 0.3 m and a force F (equal to $2 \times 30\,000 \times 0.3$ N) is provided by some pre-compression device. The upper part of Figure 2.18 shows how this could be achieved. Once the train strikes the buffer the force F no longer acts.

The free-body diagram for the train and buffer is shown in the lower part of Figure 2.18. The zero value of displacement x refers to the right-hand edge of the spring when the spring is in the unconstrained position. From Newton's second law the equation of motion for the system (buffer and train) is given by:

$$-240\,000\dot{x} - 60\,000x = 100\,000\ddot{x}$$

or

$$\ddot{x} + 2.4\dot{x} + 0.6x = 0.$$

Comparing with the standard form (equation [2.3]), we find that

$$\omega_n = 0.7746 \text{ rad/s} \quad \text{and} \quad 2\xi\omega_n = 2.4.$$

Hence $\xi = 1.55$.

The system is overdamped and to solve the differential equation we assume a solution of the form $x = \exp(\lambda t)$. The auxiliary equation is:

$$\lambda^2 + 2.4\lambda + 0.6 = 0.$$
$$\lambda_{1,2} = \{-2.4 \pm (5.76 - 2.4)^{0.5}\}/2.$$

Thus

$$\lambda_1 = -0.283485 \quad \text{and} \quad \lambda_2 = -2.116515.$$

The general solution of the differential equation is:

$$x = A \exp(-0.283485t) + B \exp(-2.116515t).$$

The first initial condition ($t = 0$) is $x = 0.3$ m; thus:

$$0.3 = A + B.$$

The second initial condition ($t = 0$) is $\dot{x} = 2$ m/s.

$$2 = -0.283485A - 2.116515B.$$

Hence

$$A = 1.43749 \qquad \text{and} \qquad B = -1.13749.$$

Therefore finally the expressions for x and $\dot{x}$ are:

$$x = 1.43749 \exp (-0.283485t) - 1.13749 \exp (-2.116515t),$$
$$\dot{x} = -0.40751 \exp (-0.283485t) + 2.40751 \exp (-2.116515t).$$

When the train comes momentarily to rest $\dot{x} = 0$. Thus

$$0.40751/2.40751 = \exp (-2.116515t + 0.283485t)$$

or

$$5.90786 = \exp (1.83303t).$$

Hence $t = 0.969$ s, and this is the time during which the train moves after impact with the buffer, before coming momentarily to rest. Putting this value for t into the expression for x we obtain:

$$x = 1.092 - 0.146 = 0.946 \text{ m}.$$

Therefore the distance reached by the train after striking the buffer before coming momentarily to rest is:

$$0.946 - 0.3 = 0.646 \text{ m}.$$

Answer   The train comes to rest after **0.646 m.**

It should be noted that, of course, the choice of a system of co-ordinates does not influence the results obtained.

Let us assume that value zero of co-ordinate x refers to the position of the buffer with pre-compression (see Fig. 2.19). As the buffer is displaced

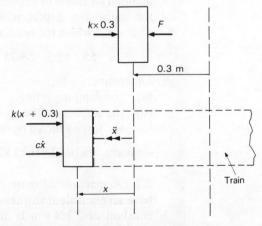

Figure 2.19   Example 2.9. Free-body diagram for buffer in equilibrium and for buffer and train in dynamic case.

from its pre-compression position by x the total spring force acting on the body (train) after impact amounts to $2 \times 30\,000(x + 0.3)$ N.

Hence the equation of motion is:

$$-60\,000(x + 0.3) - 240\,000\dot{x} = 100\,000\ddot{x}$$

or

$$\ddot{x} + 2.4\dot{x} + 0.6x = -0.18.$$

The general solution of this equation consists of the complementary function as well as the particular solution of this equation. The form of the complementary function is the same as for the previously discussed equation of motion. The particular integral in this case has a constant value $-0.18/0.6 = -0.3$.

Thus the general solution is:

$$x = -0.3 + A \exp(-0.283485t) + B \exp(-2.116515t).$$

The initial conditions $(t = 0)$ are: $x = 0$ and $\dot{x} = 2$ m/s. Hence, we obtain:

$$0 = -0.3 + A + B \quad \text{and} \quad 2 = -0.283485A - 2.116515B,$$

which give the same values for A and B as before, namely:

$$A = 1.43749 \quad \text{and} \quad B = -1.13749.$$

From equation $\dot{x} = 0$ we also obtain the same value of t of 0.969 s. This refers to the time during which the train moves after impact with the buffer before coming momentarily to rest. After substituting this value of t into the expression for x we find that for this value of time $x = 0.646$ m.

Problems

2.1 An instrument consists essentially of a mass of 80 g whose movement is controlled by a spring and viscous damper. A free, damped vibration of periodic time 0.5 s gives the following readings for successive displacements on either side of the equilibrium position at which the reading is 60:

70   55   62.5   58.75   60.62.

Determine:
(a)   the damping ratio,
(b)   the stiffness of the spring, and
(c)   the force exerted by the damper at a speed of 1 m/s.

Answers   (a) 0.215 (b) 13.2 N/m (c) 0.44 N.

2.2 A machine of mass 2 tonnes is supported on springs which have an equivalent stiffness of 25 kN/m. A dashpot with a damping constant of 1 kN s/m is attached between the machine and the ground in parallel with the springs. The machine is displaced downwards by 15 mm and then released.

Determine the maximum upward displacement from the equilibrium position, and the time taken to reach this position.

Answer   12.0 mm, 0.891 s.

2.3   An instrument of mass 4 kg is mounted on four springs and a dashpot onto a base plate. Each spring has a stiffness of 350 N/m and the dashpot has a damping constant of 15.0 N s/m.

If the base plate is displaced downwards by 20 mm and then kept in this position, determine the lowest position of the instrument relative to its original equilibrium position.

Answer   34.6 mm below the equilibrium position.

2.4   In the system shown in Figure 2.20, the link ABC is of uniform section and has a mass of 6 kg, the piston P_1 has a mass of 1.2 kg and the piston P_2 a mass of 5.3 kg. The spring S_1 has a stiffness of 3800 N/m and the spring S_2 a stiffness of 5200 N/m.

(a)   Calculate the natural frequency of small oscillations of the lever.

(b)   If the amplitudes of oscillations are to be reduced by 20% at each successive period by providing viscous damping on piston P_1, find the viscous damping force at 1 m/s.

Answers   (a) 4.86 Hz (b) 36.0 N at 1 m/s.

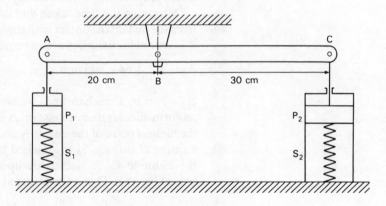

Figure 2.20   Diagram for Problem 2.4.

2.5   The signal from a displacement transducer detecting displacements of a freely vibrating body is in the form of a decaying sinusoid, as shown in Figure 2.21. Calculate the stiffness of the elastic support for the vibrating body of mass 4 kg, the damping constant and the amplitude *h* of the displacement.

Answer   115 N/m, 9.24 N s/m, 0.075 mm.

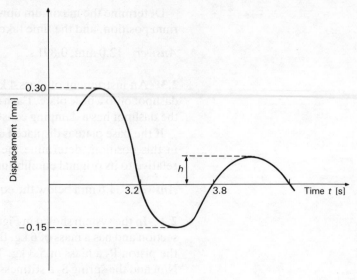

Figure 2.21 Diagram for Problem 2.5.

2.6 A steel ingot of mass 145 kg is ejected horizontally from a furnace at a speed of 0.75 m/s and is brought to rest by a hydraulic buffer incorporating a return spring. The spring exerts a force of 100 N for each metre of compression. The hydraulic piston exerts a force, proportional to the velocity, which has a value of 60 N at 1 m/s.

Determine the time taken and the distance travelled by the ingot from the instant of contact with the buffer until it first comes to rest.

Frictional resistances are to be neglected.

Answer 1.64 s, 643 mm.

2.7 Part of a mechanism is shown in Figure 2.22 and comprises a uniform circular disc of mass *m*. A spring of stiffness *k* is attached to the highest point of the disc at A and to a fixed frame at B. Similarly, a spring of stiffness 3*k* is attached between the disc centre at D and the frame at C. A viscous dashpot with a damping constant *c* is placed between D and the frame at E. The disc is able to roll on the

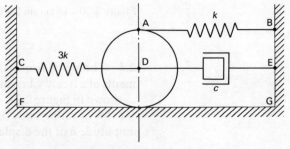

Figure 2.22 Diagram for Problem 2.7.

horizontal surface FG under the action of the spring and dashpot. AB, CDE and FG are parallel.

If the disc is caused to roll through a small angle θ_0 and then released, obtain expressions for:

    (a)   the undamped circular natural frequency,
    (b)   the damping ratio,
    (c)   the damped circular natural frequency, and
    (d)   the angular displacement as a function of time t.

Answers (a) $\omega_n = (14k/3m)^{0.5}$ (b) $\xi = c/(42mk)^{0.5}$
         (c) $\omega_d = \{(14k/3m) - c^2/(9m^2)\}^{0.5}$
         (d) $\theta = \theta_0 \exp\{-(c/3m)t\}[\cos \omega_d t$
$$+ \{\xi/(1 - \xi^2)^{0.5}\} \sin \omega_d t].$$

2.8 A gun of mass 1300 kg has recoil springs of total stiffness 500 kN/m. After firing, the gun recoils 450 mm, and for the return movement a viscous damper acts on it giving critical damping.

Show that the time for the return movement up to 20 mm from the position of static equilibrium is approximately 0.30 s.

2.9 The return mechanism of a swing door provides a torque proportional to an angle θ. The torque varies from 5 N m with the door closed ($\theta = 0°$) to 30 N m when the door is fully open ($\theta = 90°$).

When the door is closing, a viscous damping torque comes into effect at a rate of 40 N m at an angular velocity of 1 rad/s. The moment of inertia of the door about the axis of the hinge is 12.5 kg m^2.

Determine the angular position of the door after an elapsed time of 4 s.

Answer 2.21°.

2.10 The recoil mechanism of a gun consists of a spring and a dashpot formed by a piston in an oil-filled cylinder. The resistance to motion of the piston may be assumed to be proportional to the velocity of recoil.

The moving barrel of the gun, after firing, is seen to recoil a distance of 150 mm. In the subsequent motion, which is periodic, the amplitude diminishes to 12 mm after one complete cycle which occupies 1.2 s. Assuming that at the instant of firing an initial velocity is imparted to the gun barrel and that the spring support and dashpot cylinder are fixed, find the value of the initial velocity and the time taken to reach the first recoil position after firing.

Answer 1.365 m/s, 0.227 s.

2.11 A railway coach of mass 30 tonnes moves freely at 1.3 m/s into a set of stationary hydraulic buffers with internal return springs. The springs have a combined stiffness of 700 kN/m and the combined resistance to motion of the pistons in the hydraulic cylinders is proportional to the velocity and equal to 100 kN at 1 m/s.

Assuming that the springs are not initially compressed and that the coach does not rebound from the buffers, derive an expression for the displacement of the buffers from the initial static equilibrium position and hence determine:

(a) the time taken to bring the coach to rest on the first stroke, and

(b) the distance traversed in the first stroke.

Neglect the compression of the coach buffer springs.

Answers (a) 0.269 s (b) 172 mm.

2.12 An industrial buffer unit comprises a piston of mass 5 kg, a spring of stiffness 2 kN/m and a damper that provides a linear damping force of 240 N at 1 m/s. The unit forms a mass–spring–damper system with a single degree of freedom as shown schematically in Figure 2.23. The spring is initially compressed by 20 mm.

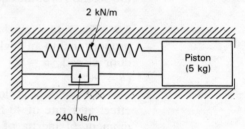

2 kN/m

Piston
(5 kg)

240 Ns/m

Figure 2.23   Diagram for Problem 2.12.

(a) Obtain the differential equation for the motion of the piston as it moves to the left in free motion and hence determine the damping ratio of the system.

(b) If a sudden impulse of 10 N s is applied to the piston, determine the distance moved by the piston before it comes momentarily to rest.

Answers (a) $\ddot{x} + 48\dot{x} + 400x = 0$, $\xi = 1.2$ (b) 28.6 mm.

2.13 In the plane mechanisms shown in Figure 2.24 a light trunnion *T* is pin-jointed to a fixed support at P. The angular motion of the trunnion causes the deflection of a torsion spring that encircles P. The torsion spring has a stiffness of 2 N m/rad. A uniform, rigid rod AGB of mass 2.4 kg and length 0.5 m passes through the trunnion and is clamped in position with mass centre G at a desired distance *x* from P. A light dashpot supplying viscous friction with a coefficient of 27 N/(m/s) is pinned to the rod at G and to the support immediately below G. The mechanism is then set in its position of static equilibrium with the rod horizontal by giving the spring an initial angular deflection.

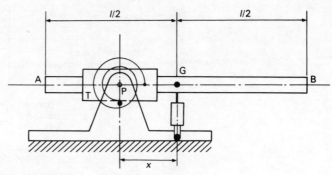

Figure 2.24   Diagram for Problem 2.13.

For small angular displacements of the rod from this position determine:

(a)   the periodic time and the logarithmic decrement of the damped oscillations of the system when $x = 0.12$ m, and

(b)   the value of x for which the motion of the system becomes critically damped.

Answers   (a) 1.47 s, 3.37 (b) 0.2 m.

2.14   The rotor of an ammeter is controlled by a torsional spring and a damper which provides a linear damping torque. The rotor has a mass of 50 g and its radius of gyration about the axis of rotation is 13.5 mm. When the rotor is displaced by 20° and released the first complete oscillation is made in 6 s, after which time the displacement has reached a maximum at 1.6°. Determine

(a)   the torsional stiffness of the spring and the damping constant at the damper.

If the rotor is initially at rest and receives a sudden impulse that causes it to swing through 10°, determine:

(b)   the time taken to swing through 10°, and

(c)   the energy supplied by the impulse.

Answers   (a) 11.61×10^{-6} N m/rad, 7.67×10^{-6} N m s/rad
(b)   1.14 s
(c)   0.460 μJ.

2.15   A seat in a truck is to be mounted on a spring and damper so that the driver can be protected from vibrations generated by the engine. A simple model with a single degree of freedom, as shown in Figure 2.25, is constructed for the system. The seat is regarded as a rigid mass of 40 kg supported by a spring of 18 kN/m and a viscous dashpot which provides a damping force of 600 N at 1 m/s. A man of mass 80 kg sits on the seat free of the ground.

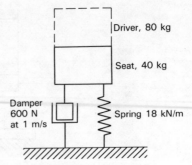

Figure 2.25   Diagram for Problem 2.15.

(a)   Obtain the differential equation defining the motion of the system and hence determine the damping ratio.

(b)   If the driver slips off the seat without imparting a vertical impulse to it, determine the new damping ratio and the maximum distance that the seat subsequently moves upwards from the initial position.

(c)   Sketch the displacement of the seat against time after the driver has left.

Answers   (a) $\ddot{x} + 5\dot{x} + 150x = 0$, $\xi = 0.204$
(b) $\xi = 0.354$, 56.9 mm (43.6 + 13.3).

2.16   The mechanism shown in Figure 2.26 is used to measure the speed of a shaft A which passes through a housing B containing a

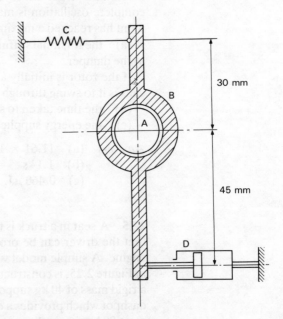

Figure 2.26   Diagram for Problem 2.16.

viscous fluid. The spring C confines the movement of the housing to small angular displacements with respect to its datum position at zero shaft speed, and a viscous damper D is incorporated as shown.

Details of the mechanism are:

moment of inertia of housing B and attachments about the shaft axis	$0.1 \times 10^{-3} \, \text{kg m}^2$
stiffness of spring C	$40 \, \text{N/m}$
viscous frictional couple/angular speed, due to fluid in housing B	$0.15 \times 10^{-3} \, \text{N m s/rad}$
viscous damping coefficient of damper D	$0.38 \, \text{N s/m}$

Find the angular displacement of the housing from its datum position when the shaft is running at a steady speed of 10 Hz. Given that the shaft is then stopped suddenly, derive an expression for the angular displacement of the housing at any time t thereafter.

Answer $0.262 \, \text{rad}$, $\theta = 0.27 \exp(-4.59t) \cos(18.4t - 0.244)$.

2.17   Figure 2.27 shows a safety door, of mass 200 kg, which is designed to move freely in vertical guides and which is held in the open position, the normal position, by a pin P. In an emergency the pin is withdrawn and the door falls freely through a height of 0.35 m before striking and adhering to a buffer mechanism. This mechanism consists of linear springs, initially unstressed, of total stiffness 7.2 kN/m, and a viscous dashpot with a damping constant of 2.4 kN/(m/s); the total mass of the buffer is negligible when compared with that of the door. At the instant of maximum compression of the buffer a latch holds the door in the closed, or emergency position.

Determine the time taken after withdrawal of the pin for the door to reach the closed position in an emergency and the corresponding maximum compression of the buffer.

Answer   0.710 s, 11.5 mm.

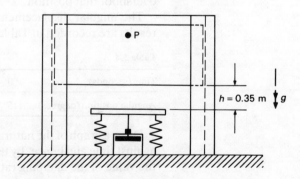

Figure 2.27   Diagram for Problem 2.17.

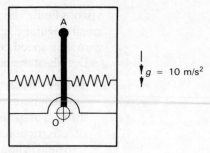

Figure 2.28 Diagram for Problem 2.18.

2.18 Figure 2.28 shows a simple instrument situated in a gravitational field of 10 m/s². A pendulum consisting of a uniform rod OA, of mass 0.3 kg and length 100 mm, is pinned to the instrument case at O and is held vertically in static equilibrium by two springs, each of stiffness 750 N/m. The axes of the springs are horizontal and at a distance of 20 mm above O. When the rod oscillates and has an angular velocity $\dot{\theta}$, there is a couple caused by friction. This couple has a moment which amounts to $c\dot{\theta}$, where c is a constant equal to 0.03 N m s.

Determine the frequency of small oscillations of the pendulum when the case is:

(a) at rest, and   (b) in free fall.

(c) Find the magnitude of the vertical acceleration of the case for which the motion of the pendulum in the gravitational field of 10 m/s² becomes critically damped.

Answers (a) 2.387 Hz (b) 3.082 Hz (c) 15 m/s².

2.19 A circular disc was suspended by a torsion wire from a fixed support. When the disc was allowed to make free vibrations in the horizontal plane about the axis of the wire it was observed that 20 complete oscillations took 157.1 s. The disc was immersed in a bath of heavy oil. When the disc was given an angular displacement about the vertical axis of the wire and released, it was observed that the disc returned slowly to the equilibrium position, but did not overshoot that position.

The angular displacement of the disc was timed over 10 s. The results are recorded in Table 2.4.

Table 2.4

Time (seconds)	0	1	2	3	4	5	6	7	8	9	10
Angular position (degrees)	115	107	99	91	84	77	71	66	61	56	52

Draw a graph of the natural logarithm of the angular displacement against time and hence, by using the method of least squares, obtain the value of the damping ratio.

Answer 5.05.

3

Forced vibrations of systems with a single degree of freedom

The vibrations described in the last chapter were free, and decayed to zero, provided that some damping was present. In this chapter we are concerned with vibrations of damped systems that are maintained as long as energy is supplied.

The basic system is similar to that presented in Chapter 2, as shown in Figure 3.1(a), but now additionally a force $F(t)$—a force as a function of time—is applied to the body of mass m. The equation of motion (see the free-body diagram of Figure 3.1(b) is in this case:

$$F(t) - ky - c\dot{y} = m\ddot{y}.$$

And

$$\ddot{y} + 2\xi\omega_n\dot{y} + \omega_n^2 y = F(t)/m. \tag{3.1}$$

3.1 The forcing function

Most of the forcing functions considered here will be harmonic, for example:

$$F(t) = F_0 \sin \omega t. \tag{3.2}$$

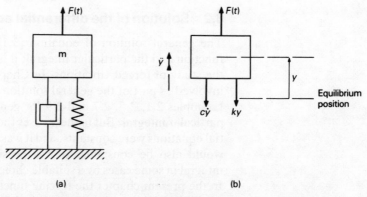

(a) (b)

Figure 3.1 (a) System with a single degree of freedom, with excitation force $F(t)$, (b) free-body diagram for system shown in (a).

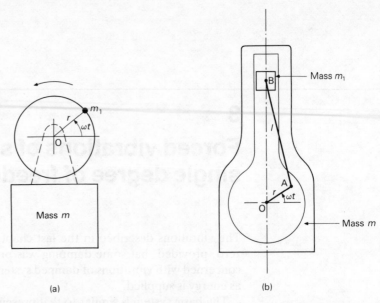

Figure 3.2 Excitation forces proportional to ω^2. (a) Rotating out-of-balance mass m_1, (b) reciprocating mass m_1 ($r \ll l$).

In this case we have a sinusoid of constant amplitude F_0 and circular frequency ω. Another example is:

$$F(t) = m_1 r \omega^2 \sin \omega t. \tag{3.3}$$

This is a common type of forcing or exciting function which occurs when there is an out-of-balance rotating mass m_1 at a distance r from the axis of rotation, as shown in Figure 3.2(a). In the engine mechanism of the reciprocating type (Figure 3.2(b)) the vertical component of the force acting on the larger body of mass m (the cylinder and frame of the engine, etc.) is $m_1 r \omega^2 \sin \omega t$, provided that the connecting rod AB is long compared with the length r of the crank OA.

3.2 Solution of the differential equation of forced motion

The general solution of equation [3.1] comprises the complementary function and the particular integral; it is the latter which is important in the study of forced vibrations. In Chapter 2 the particular integral was involved as part of the general solution of the differential equation. See Examples 2.1, 2.5, 2.7 and 2.9 for general solutions which comprise a particular integral. But in these cases the right-hand sides of the differential equations were constants, and it was clear that the particular integrals would also be constants. It was possible to eliminate the particular integral in some cases by a suitable choice of datum for the displacement. In the present chapter the forcing functions of equations [3.2] and [3.3] are harmonic and, when they are included in the differential equation of [3.1], the particular integral (or the particular solution) of that equation is similarly harmonic. Once this is realized it becomes easy to determine the particular integral.

The particular integral of equation [3.1] for damped and forced vibration is often called the steady-state solution, because this is the component of the solution that does not decay in time. It persists in time, whereas the second component of the solution, the complementary function or transient solution, decays exponentially in time. In practice for the case of damped, forced vibrations the complementary function is of importance only during the early stage of the vibration, and therefore it is called the transient solution.

We will assume for the particular integral the form:

$$y = Y \sin (\omega t - \Phi) \qquad [3.4]$$

although a cosine form would be just as acceptable. In equation [3.4] Y is an amplitude and Φ is a phase angle. For $\dot{y}$ and $\ddot{y}$ we can write:

$$\dot{y} = \omega Y \sin (\omega t - \Phi + \pi/2),$$
$$\ddot{y} = \omega^2 Y \sin (\omega t - \Phi + \pi).$$

(Expand out the above two expressions to check that they agree with the usual form of the derivatives of expression [3.4].) Assuming the forcing function to be the same as in equation [3.2], we have for the equation of motion:

$$\ddot{y} + 2\xi\omega_n\dot{y} + \omega_n^2 y = (F_0/m) \sin \omega t. \qquad [3.5]$$

Substituting the above expressions for y, $\dot{y}$ and $\ddot{y}$ in equation [3.5] we obtain:

$$\omega^2 Y \sin (\omega t - \Phi + \pi) + 2\xi\omega\omega_n Y \sin (\omega t - \Phi + \pi/2)$$
$$+ \omega_n^2 Y \sin (\omega t - \Phi) = (F_0/m) \sin \omega t. \qquad [3.6]$$

Each individual component of equation [3.6] can be represented by a phasor. These phasors have magnitudes and phase relationships to each other. They can be visualized, as shown in Figure 3.3, by means of vectors

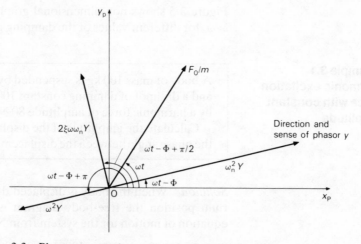

Figure 3.3 Phasors as rotating vectors for forced vibration.

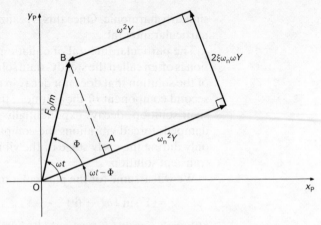

Figure 3.4   Phasor diagram for forced vibration.

rotating about point O in an anti-clockwise sense. In general phasors can be scalars as well as vectors. The terms in equation [3.6] are the projections of the rotating vectors on the vertical (y_P) co-ordinate, as shown in Figure 3.3. These projections are y_P components of the appropriate vectors, and these vectors are the phasors. The phasors (vectors) corresponding to the appropriate terms of equation [3.6], and shown in Figure 3.3, may be put together to construct the phasor diagram of Figure 3.4. From the right-angled triangle OAB in Figure 3.4 we obtain:

$$F_0/m = Y\{(\omega_n^2 - \omega^2)^2 + (2\xi\omega\omega_n)^2\}^{0.5}$$

or

$$Y = \frac{F_0/(m\omega_n^2)}{[\{1 - (\omega/\omega_n)^2\}^2 + (2\xi\omega/\omega_n)^2]^{0.5}}.$$ [3.7]

Similarly the angle Φ is given by:

$$\tan \Phi = (2\xi\omega/\omega_n)/\{1 - (\omega/\omega_n)^2\}.$$ [3.7a]

Figure 3.5 shows non-dimensional graphs of $Y/(F_0/m\omega_n^2)$ and Φ against ω/ω_n for different values of the damping ratio ξ.

Example 3.1
Harmonic excitation force with constant amplitude

A body of mass 100 kg is suspended by a spring of stiffness 30 kN/m and a dashpot of damping constant 1000 N s/m. Vibration is excited by a harmonic force of amplitude 80 N and frequency 3 Hz.
Calculate the amplitude of the displacement for the vibration and the phase angle between the displacement and the excitation force.

Solution   When the body is displaced downwards by y from its equilibrium position the free-body diagram is as shown in Figure 3.6. The equation of motion for the system from Newton's second law is:

$$80 \sin (2\pi \times 3t) - 1000\dot{y} - 30\,000y = 100\ddot{y}.$$

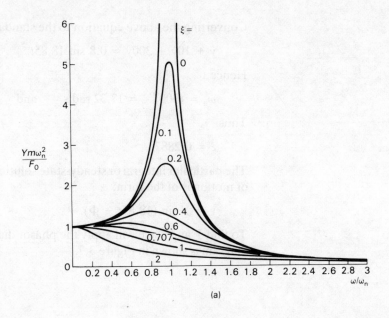

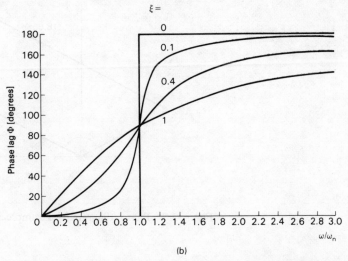

Figure 3.5 (a) Amplitude of displacement Y in non-dimensional form for steady-state motion and (b) phase angle Φ plotted against non-dimensional frequency ω/ω_n when $F(t) = F_0 \sin \omega t$.

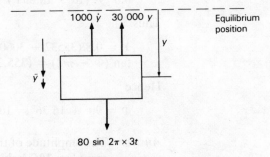

Figure 3.6 Free-body diagram for Example 3.1.

Converting the above equation to the standard form we obtain:

$$\ddot{y} + 10\dot{y} + 300y = 0.8 \sin 18.85t.$$

Hence,

$$\omega_n = (300)^{0.5} = 17.32 \text{ rad/s} \qquad \text{and} \qquad 2\xi\omega_n = 10.$$

Thus

$$\xi = 0.2887.$$

The particular integral or steady-state solution of the considered equation of motion is of the form:

$$y = Y \sin (18.85t - \Phi).$$

To find Y and Φ we will apply the phasor diagram approach. The phasor diagram is shown in Figure 3.7.

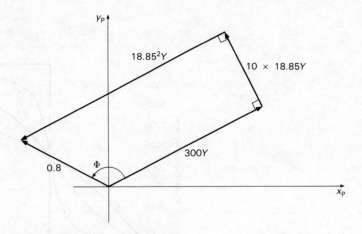

Figure 3.7   Phasor diagram for Example 3.1.

Hence

$$0.8^2 = (10 \times 18.85Y)^2 + (-300Y + 18.85^2Y)^2.$$

Thus

$$Y = 0.8/(35532 + 3060.6)^{0.5} = 4.07 \times 10^{-3} \text{ m} = 4.07 \text{ mm}.$$
$$\tan (\Phi - \pi/2) = (355.32 - 300)/188.5 = 0.29347.$$

Hence

$$\Phi = 90° + 16.36° = 106.36°.$$

Answer   The amplitude of the displacement is **4.1 mm** and the displacement lags **106°** behind the excitation force.

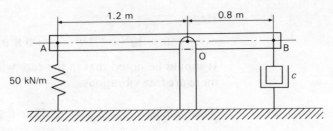

Figure 3.8   Diagram for Example 3.2.

**Example 3.2
Forced vibration of a
beam rotating about a
fixed axis**

In Figure 3.8 a slender rigid beam AB of mass 80 kg and length 2 m
is shown supported in the horizontal position by a spring of stiffness
50 kN/m at A and by a frictionless pivot at O, 1.2 m away from the
spring. A viscous damper with a damping constant c is positioned,
as shown, at the other end B.

(a)   Establish the differential equation which applies when the
beam executes free damped oscillations of small amplitude.

(b)   Determine the value of the damping constant c in order to
achieve a damping ratio ξ of 0.5.

(c)   A sinusoidal force of amplitude 200 N and frequency 13 Hz
is applied vertically at A. With the value of c obtained above
determine the amplitude of the small steady-state oscillations of the
beam.

Solution   (a)   When the beam is displaced through an angle θ in a
clockwise sense, the free-body diagram is as shown in Figure 3.9. First of
all we calculate I_O, the moment of inertia of the beam about the fixed axis
through O:

$$I_O = 80 \times 2^2/12 + 80 \times 0.2^2 = 29.867 \text{ kg m}^2.$$

Let us take moments about the fixed rotation axis through O and write
down the equation of motion for the beam:

$$\Sigma M_O = I_O\ddot{\theta}.$$

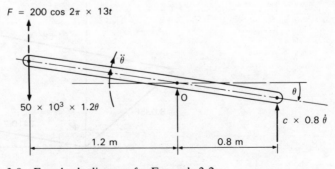

Figure 3.9   Free-body diagram for Example 3.2.

Hence

$$-50 \times 10^3 \times 1.2^2\theta - c \times 0.8^2\dot{\theta} = 29.867\ddot{\theta}.$$

It should be noted that in the case when the excitation force F is zero, there are free vibrations.

Answer to part (a) $\ddot{\theta} + 0.02143c\dot{\theta} + 2410.7\theta = 0.$

(b)   Let us compare the equation written as the answer to part (a) with its standard form:

$$\ddot{\theta} + 2\xi\omega_n\dot{\theta} + \omega_n^2\theta = 0.$$

Thus

$$\omega_n = 2410.7^{0.5} = 49.10 \text{ rad/s.}$$

And $2\xi\omega_n = 0.02143c$. With $\xi = 0.5$, $c = 2 \times 0.5 \times 49.1/0.02143$.

Answer to part (b)   The damping constant $c = $ **2291 N** at 1 m/s.

(c)   With the excitation force applied at A the new equation of motion is:

$$1.2 \times 200 \cos 81.68t - 50 \times 10^3 \times 1.2^2\theta - 2291 \times 0.8^2\dot{\theta} = 29.867\ddot{\theta}$$

or

$$\ddot{\theta} + 49.1\dot{\theta} + 2410.7\theta = 8.0356 \cos 81.68t.$$

The steady-state solution of the above differential equation may be written as:

$$\theta = X \cos (81.68t - \Phi).$$

Hence we obtain the phasor diagram shown in Figure 3.10.
From the diagram of Figure 3.10, we have

$$8.0356^2 = (4010.5X)^2 + (4260.9X)^2.$$

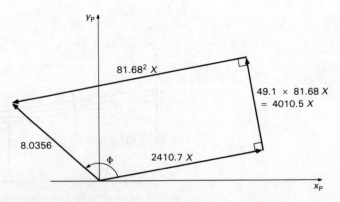

Figure 3.10   Phasor diagram for Example 3.2.

Hence

$$X = 8.0356/(4010.5^2 + 4260.9^2)^{0.5} = 0.00137 \text{ rad (or } 0.079°).$$

Answer to part (c) The amplitude of the beam's steady-state oscillations is **0.079°**.

The next example also concerns a beam. There is, however, a difference between the problems, namely the piston of the dashpot now has a mass.

**Example 3.3
Beam problem in
which piston of
dashpot has mass**

The beam illustrated in Figure 3.11 has a mass of 4 kg and a radius of gyration of 70 mm about the centre of mass G. One end of the beam is pivoted at A, and at the other end B the beam is supported by a spring of stiffness 20 kN/m which maintains the beam horizontal when it is in the equilibrium position. A harmonic force of amplitude 120 N and frequency 5 Hz is applied to the end B. Damping is provided by a dashpot with a damping constant of 400 N s/m. The piston C of the dashpot has a mass of 1.2 kg and is attached to the beam by a light, rigid link at G.

Determine the following magnitudes:
(a)   the undamped natural frequency of the vibrations,
(b)   the damping ratio,
(c)   the amplitude of the displacement at B for steady-state vibrations, and
(d)   the amplitude of the force in the link CG, also for steady-state vibrations.

Solution There are two approaches to this problem: either we can treat the beam AB and piston C individually and draw separate free-body diagrams for the beam and the piston, or we can consider the beam and the piston as a whole by adding the piston mass to that of the beam at G.

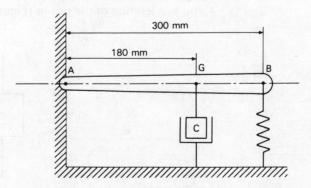

Figure 3.11   Diagram for Example 3.3.

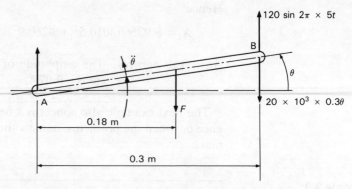

Figure 3.12 Free-body diagram for the beam in Example 3.3.

We should also realize that CG is a light link. The first approach is more instructive and in any case we are encouraged to do this because the question concerns the force acting on the link GC.

The free-body diagram for the beam AB is given in Figure 3.12, where θ is the angular anti-clockwise displacement of the beam.

F is the force acting on the link GC, as shown in Figure 3.12. Rotation occurs about a fixed axis through A, hence the equation of motion for the beam is:

$$\Sigma M_A = I_A\ddot{\theta}.$$

Additionally we know that:

$$I_A = I_G + md^2 \quad \text{(parallel-axes theorem)}$$
$$= 4 \times 0.07^2 + 4 \times 0.18^2 = 0.1492 \text{ kg m}^2.$$

Therefore, the equation of motion of the beam is:

$$0.3 \times 120 \sin 10\pi t - 0.3(20 \times 10^3 \times 0.3\theta) - 0.18F = 0.1492\ddot{\theta}$$

or

$$36 \sin 31.42t - 1800\theta - 0.18F = 0.1492\ddot{\theta}. \qquad [3.8]$$

Figure 3.13 shows the free-body diagram for the piston C. The velocity and acceleration of the piston (Figure 3.13) are $0.18\dot{\theta}$ and $0.18\ddot{\theta}$, respec-

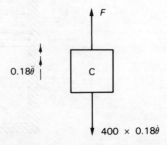

Figure 3.13 Free-body diagram for the piston in Example 3.3.

tively. Applying Newton's second law, we obtain the equation of motion for the piston C:

$$F - 400 \times 0.18\dot{\theta} = 1.2 \times 0.18\ddot{\theta}$$

or

$$F - 72\dot{\theta} = 0.216\ddot{\theta}. \qquad [3.9]$$

Let us multiply equation [3.9] by 0.18 and then add the resulting equation to [3.8] to eliminate F.

$$36 \sin 31.42t - 1800\theta - 12.96\dot{\theta} = 0.03888\ddot{\theta} + 0.1492\ddot{\theta} \qquad [3.10]$$

or

$$\ddot{\theta} + 68.91\dot{\theta} + 9570.4\theta = 191.41 \sin 31.42t. \qquad [3.11]$$

The above equation is compared with the standard form, and hence

$$\omega_n^2 = 9570.4 \quad \text{and} \quad \omega_n = 97.83 \text{ rad/s.} \quad f_n = 15.57 \text{ Hz.}$$
$$2\xi\omega_n = 68.91, \quad \text{thus} \quad \xi = 68.91/(2 \times 97.83) = 0.352.$$

Answers (a) Undamped natural frequency is **15.6 Hz.**
(b) Damping ratio is **0.352.**

We can use the phasor method to find the steady-state solution of the differential equation [3.11]. The steady-state solution is of the form:

$$\theta = X \sin (31.42t - \Phi).$$

Hence,

$$\dot{\theta} = 31.42X \sin (31.42t - \Phi + \pi/2).$$

And

$$\ddot{\theta} = 31.42^2 X \sin (31.42t - \Phi + \pi).$$

Substituting the above expressions for θ, $\dot{\theta}$ and $\ddot{\theta}$ in equation [3.11] one obtains:

$$31.42^2 X \sin (31.42t - \Phi + \pi)$$
$$+ 68.91 \times 31.42X \sin (31.42t - \Phi + \pi/2)$$
$$+ 9570.4X \sin (31.42t - \Phi) = 191.41 \sin 31.42t. \qquad [3.12]$$

Each term of the differential equation [3.11] is now represented (see equation [3.12]) by a phasor with the angle in the sine terms giving information on the phase. The phasor diagram for any instant in time is as shown in Figure 3.14. Applying Pythagoras's theorem to triangle OAB:

$$191.41^2 = (68.91 \times 31.42X)^2 + (9570.4X - 31.42^2 X)^2$$
$$X = 191.41/\{(9570.4 - 31.42^2)^2 + (68.91 \times 31.42)^2\}^{0.5}$$
$$= 2.16 \times 10^{-2} \text{ rad.}$$

Answer to part (c) Amplitude of displacement for steady-state vibration at B is $2.16 \times 10^{-2} \times 300$ mm or **6.5 mm.**

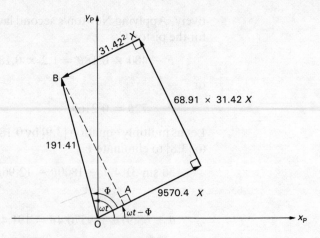

Figure 3.14   Phasor diagram for Example 3.3.

To find the force F in the link GC we must analyse equation [3.9]. This equation may be represented by phasors; hence

$$F = 72 \times 31.42X \sin (31.42t - \Phi + \pi/2)$$
$$+ 0.216 \times 31.42^2X \sin (31.42t - \Phi + \pi).$$

The phasor diagram representing the above equation is shown in Figure 3.15. Hence

$$F = X\{(0.216 \times 31.42^2)^2 + (72 \times 31.42)^2\}^{0.5} = 49.1 \, \text{N}.$$

Answer to part (d)   Amplitude of the force in the link GC for steady-state vibration is **49.1 N.**

At the beginning of this procedure for solving the problem it was mentioned that an alternative would be to consider the piston and the beam as a whole with the mass of the piston added to that of the beam at

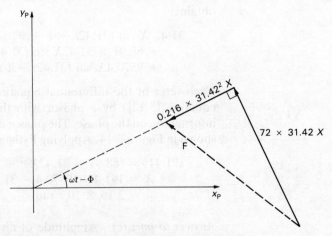

Figure 3.15   Phasor diagram to obtain force in link GC.

G. If we do this I'_A, the new moment of inertia of the beam and the piston combined is given by:

$$I'_A = I_A + 0.18^2 \times 1.2 = 0.1492 + 0.03888$$
$$= 0.1881 \text{ kg m}^2.$$

The two components of I'_A are the same as the coefficients of $\ddot{\theta}$ found on the right-hand side of equation [3.10]. This equation could now be obtained directly by considering moments about the rotation axis through A and writing down the equation of motion for the system (beam and piston). The force F should be replaced by the damping force $400 \times 0.18\dot{\theta}$ (see the free-body diagram of Figure 3.12).

Example 3.4
Forced vibration of a moving-coil d.c. ammeter

A moving coil d.c. ammeter has a rotor controlled by a torsion spring and a viscous damper. The angular displacement of the rotor is directly proportional to the current. The undamped natural frequency of the system is 4 Hz, and the damping is critical.

A current of constant amplitude is passed through the meter. When the current has zero frequency, the meter indication is 1 A. Determine the meter indication when the frequency of the current is 6 Hz.

Solution A moving-coil d.c. ammeter is constructed as shown in Figure 3.16. When a direct current i passes through the coil, a torque T proportional to i acts on the coil, i.e., $T = Ki$, where K is a constant. This torque is normally equal to a restoring torque of $s\theta$ caused by the presence of the torsion spring of stiffness s. The angle θ is the angle the coil turns through. So $i = (s/K)\theta$ or current is proportional to angle θ. This is the principle of the d.c. ammeter.

When an alternating current (such that $i = I_0 \sin \omega t$) is passed through the coil the situation is different, because the value of the torque is now fluctuating. Let us denote the moment of inertia of the moving parts (coil, former and pointer) about the fixed rotation axis through the pivot as J, and the damping torque as $c\dot{\theta}$. The damping is often provided electrically

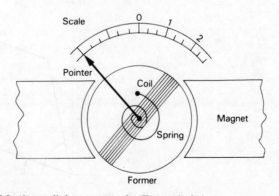

Figure 3.16   Moving coil dc ammeter for Example 3.4.

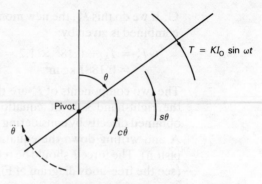

Figure 3.17 Torques acting on the iron core of the d.c. ammeter.

rather than mechanically. The torques acting on the rotating parts of the meter are now as shown in Figure 3.17.

Taking moments about the fixed axis of rotation through the pivot, we obtain the equation of motion for the system:

$$KI_0 \sin \omega t - s\theta - c\dot{\theta} = J\ddot{\theta}$$

or

$$\ddot{\theta} + (c/J)\dot{\theta} + (s/J)\theta = (KI_0/J)\sin \omega t. \qquad [3.13]$$

It is assumed that the damping ratio ξ is 1 and the undamped circular natural frequency ω_n is $2\pi \times 4$ rad/s. Equation [3.13] could be written in the standard form:

$$\ddot{\theta} + 2\xi\omega_n\dot{\theta} + \omega_n^2\theta = (KI_0/J) \sin \omega t.$$

Thus

$$\ddot{\theta} + 50.27\dot{\theta} + 631.65\theta = (KI_0/J) \sin \omega t. \qquad [3.14]$$

The steady-state solution of equation [3.14] is of the form

$$\theta = Y \sin (\omega t - \Phi),$$

where Y is the amplitude and Φ is a phase angle. The phasor diagram for equation [3.14] is shown in Figure 3.18.

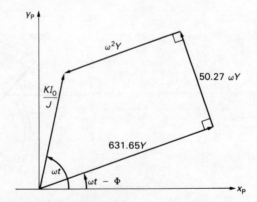

Figure 3.18 Phasor diagram for Example 3.4.

From the phasor diagram we can obtain Y in terms of ω:

$$Y = (KI_0/J)/\{(50.27\omega)^2 + (631.65 - \omega^2)^2\}^{0.5}.$$

When the frequency is zero the amplitude Y_0 is given by:

$$Y_0 = (KI_0/J)/631.65.$$

This is the displacement when a direct current I_0 – in this case 1 A – is applied to the coil. When the frequency of the current is 6 Hz, the circular frequency $\omega = 2\pi \times 6$ rad/s and the amplitude Y_6 is given by:

$$Y_6 = (KI_0/J)/[(50.27 \times 12\pi)^2 + \{631.65 - (12\pi)^2\}^2]^{0.5}.$$

Hence

$$Y_6/Y_0 = 631.65/[(50.27 \times 12\pi)^2 + \{631.65 - (12\pi)^2\}^2]^{0.5}$$
$$= 0.308.$$

At zero frequency (d.c.) the correct reading of 1 A is obtained on the scale. When an alternating current of frequency 6 Hz and amplitude 1 A is applied to the meter the pointer indicates 0.308 A. Note that there will be no oscillation of the needle, because the damping is critical. One learns from this example that a d.c. ammeter is unsatisfactory for measuring alternating currents.

Answer   Meter indication is **0.308 A.**

3.3   Excitation force proportional to the square of the frequency

If an excitation force of the form given in equation [3.3], associated with the system shown in Figure 3.2, is applied to the spring–mass–damper system, then the equation of motion (equation [3.1]) is

$$\ddot{y} + 2\xi\omega_n\dot{y} + \omega_n^2 y = (1/m)(m_1r\omega^2) \sin \omega t.$$

The steady-state solution has the form of equation [3.4]. From a phasor diagram an expression for Y is given by:

$$Y = \frac{(m_1r/m)(\omega/\omega_n)^2}{[\{1 - (\omega/\omega_n)^2\}^2 + (2\xi\omega/\omega_n)^2]^{0.5}}. \tag{3.15}$$

The expression for the phase angle Φ has the same form as that given by equation [3.7(a)]. In Figure 3.19 plots of $Y/(m_1r/m)$ against ω/ω_n are shown for different values of ξ. These curves are different from those of Figure 3.5. When the excitation force is proportional to ω^2, the frequency corresponding to the maximum displacement (the resonant frequency) increases as ξ increases, as long as $\xi < 0.707$, as may be seen in Figure 3.19. In Figure 3.5 it is shown that the resonant frequency decreases with increasing ξ. One can observe in Figure 3.19 that when ω/ω_n tends to infinity Y attains a value of m_1r/m.

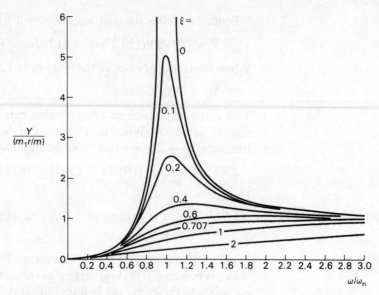

Figure 3.19 Amplitude of displacement Y in non-dimensional form for steady-state motion when $F(t) = m_1 r\omega^2 \sin \omega t$.

Example 3.5
Power output of a
mechanical shaker

A mechanical shaker, illustrated in Figure 3.20, contains two shafts which rotate at the same speed in opposite directions. The out-of-balance of each shaft is equivalent to a mass m of 1.15 kg at a radius r of 50 mm. The shaker is attached to a rigid plate that is supported upon two vibration isolators, each of which has the combined characteristics of a linear spring and a dashpot for which the damping constant is c. The system can be assumed to have one degree of freedom in the vertical direction.

With the shaker running at a constant speed of 2000 rev/min, it is observed that the amplitude of steady-state forced vibration of the plate is 6.0 mm and that the phase angle between the vertical shaking force and the plate displacement is 30°.

Determine:
(a) the value of the constant c for each isolator, and
(b) the mean power output of the shaker.

Solution The vertical component of the force acting on the rotation shaft is $mr\omega^2 \cos \omega t$. Here, $m = 1.15$ kg, $r = 0.050$ m, and $\omega = 2\pi(2000/60) = 209.44$ rad/s. There are two shafts so the vertical component of the total force is given by:

$$2 \times 1.15 \times 0.050 \times (209.44)^2 \cos 209.44t = 5044.5 \cos 209.44t \text{ N}.$$

(Note that, because of the arrangement of the masses m on the shafts, the vertical components of the forces add directly and the horizontal components cancel out.)

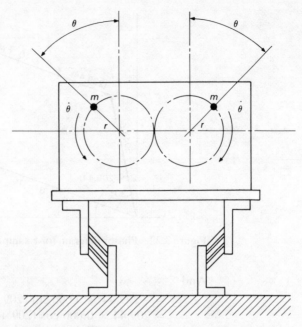

Figure 3.20   Diagram for Example 3.5.

The free-body diagram for the shaker is given in Figure 3.21, where the displacement of the shaker is y, measured upwards from its equilibrium position. In the equation of motion for the shaker M denotes the total mass of the shaker and k is the stiffness of one isolator. Hence:

$$5044.5 \cos 209.44t - 2ky - 2c\dot{y} = M\ddot{y}$$

or

$$M\ddot{y} + 2c\dot{y} + 2ky = 5044.5 \cos 209.44t. \qquad [3.16]$$

We are informed that the displacement amplitude of the steady-state vibration is 6 mm and that the phase difference between excitation force and displacement is 30°. Hence we may write the steady-state solution of the differential equation [3.16] as:

$$y = 0.006 \cos (209.44t - \pi/6).$$

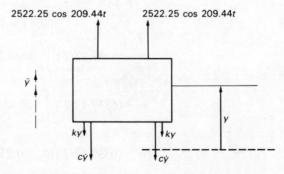

Figure 3.21   Free-body diagram for shaker in Example 3.5.

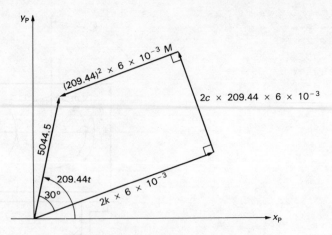

Figure 3.22   Phasor diagram for Example 3.5.

And
$$\dot{y} = -209.44 \times 0.006 \sin (209.44t - \pi/6)$$
$$= 209.44 \times 0.006 \cos (209.44t - \pi/6 + \pi/2).$$

Also
$$\ddot{y} = (209.44)^2 \times 0.006 \cos (209.44t - \pi/6 + \pi).$$

The resulting phasor diagram is as shown in Figure 3.22. Hence

$$5044.5 \sin 30° = 2c \times 209.44 \times 0.006 \qquad \text{and} \qquad c = 1003.6 \text{ N s/m.}$$

Answer to part (a)   The damping constant c is **1004 N s/m.**

In general power is expressed by force $\times$ velocity. In this case the force is the excitation force caused by the rotating out-of-balance mass, and the velocity is $\dot{y}$. Thus, during the time period T (where $T = 2\pi/209.44$), the mean power output is:

$$\frac{1}{T} \int_0^T F(t)\dot{y} \, dt$$

$$= \frac{1}{T} \int_0^T 5044.5 \cos (209.44t)$$

$$\times (-1)209.44 \times 0.006 \sin (209.44t - \pi/6) \, dt$$

$$= -(6339.12/T) \int_0^T \{\cos 209.44t(\sin 209.44t \times \cos \pi/6$$
$$- \cos 209.44t \times \sin \pi/6)\} \, dt$$

$$= -(6339.12/T) \int_0^T \{0.4330 \sin 418.88t$$
$$- 0.25(1 + \cos 418.88t)\} \, dt$$

$$= -(6339.12/T)\{0 - 0.25(T + 0)\} = 1585 \text{ W.}$$

Answer to part (b)   The mean power output is **1585 W.**

Example 3.6
Vibration of beam
excited by rotating
out-of-balance mass

A beam is pivoted at one end and supported at the other by rubber in shear which acts as a combined spring and damper. The spring is linear and the damper gives viscous equivalent damping. Excitation of small amplitude forced vibrations is caused by an out-of-balance rotor of mass m_1 with its centre of mass at a distance r from the axis of rotation. The rotor has a speed of ω rad/s. A diagram of the set-up is given in Figure 3.23.

Show that the equation of motion of the system is

$$(I_O + m_1 s^2)\ddot{\theta} + cl^2\dot{\theta} + kl^2\theta = (m_1 r s\omega^2) \sin \omega t,$$

where θ is the angle of rotation of the beam,
  I_O is the moment of inertia of the beam about the rotation axis through the pivot,
  c is the equivalent viscous damping coefficient of the rubber,
  k is the spring stiffness of the rubber,
  l is the length of the beam,
  s is the distance between the pivot and the rotor bearings.

Show that if the steady-state solution is of the form:

$$\theta = \theta_0 \sin (\omega t - \Phi)$$

then

$$\theta_0 = \frac{(m_1 r s\omega^2)/\{(I_O + m_1 s^2)\omega_n^2\}}{[\{1 - (\omega/\omega_n)^2\}^2 + \{2\xi(\omega/\omega_n)\}^2]^{0.5}}$$

and

$$\tan \Phi = 2\xi(\omega/\omega_n)/\{1 - (\omega/\omega_n)^2\},$$

where ξ is the damping ratio and ω_n is the undamped circular natural frequency.

For a particular system the undamped natural frequency is 15.5 Hz, ξ is 0.05, l is 600 mm, s is 440 mm, m_1 is 1.6 kg and the product $m_1 r$ is 1.0×10^{-3} kg m.

The beam is uniform, of density 7.8×10^3 kg/m³, and is 600 mm long, 153 mm wide and 6 mm thick.

Estimate the displacements at a point 300 mm from the pivot for frequencies of 15 Hz and 15.5 Hz.

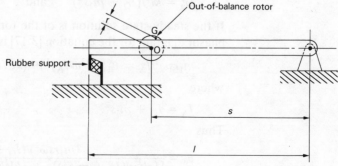

Figure 3.23   Diagram for Example 3.6.

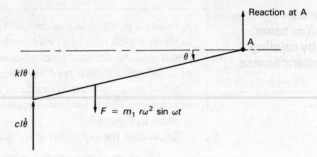

Figure 3.24 Free-body diagram for the beam in Example 3.6.

Solution When the beam is displaced by an angle θ anti-clockwise the forces on the beam are as shown in the free-body diagram of Figure 3.24. If I_A is the moment of inertia of the beam and rotor (where the rotor mass is treated as a point mass) about the rotation axis through the pivot A, then

$$I_A = I_O + m_1 s^2.$$

Analysing moments about the fixed rotation axis through the pivot, we have:

$$-kl^2\theta - cl^2\dot{\theta} + sm_1 r\omega^2 \sin \omega t = (I_0 + m_1 s^2)\ddot{\theta}.$$

Hence

$$(I_O + m_1 s^2)\ddot{\theta} + cl^2\dot{\theta} + kl^2\theta = (m_1 rs\omega^2)\sin \omega t. \qquad [3.17]$$

Equation [3.17] is the answer in the required form. It will also be useful to divide both sides of equation [3.17] by $(I_O + m_1 s^2)$ and to compare the resulting equation with the standard form:

$$\ddot{\theta} + 2\xi\omega_n \dot{\theta} + \omega_n^2\theta = 0.$$

We have:

$$\ddot{\theta} + \{cl^2/(I_O + m_1 s^2)\}\dot{\theta} + \{kl^2/(I_O + m_1 s^2)\}\theta$$
$$= \{(m_1 rs\omega^2)/(I_O + m_1 s^2)\} \sin \omega t.$$

Thus

$$\omega_n^2 = kl^2/(I_O + m_1 s^2) \qquad \text{and} \qquad 2\xi\omega_n = cl^2/(I_O + m_1 s^2).$$

If the steady-state solution is of the form $\theta = \theta_0 \sin (\omega t - \Phi)$ then the phasor diagram for the equation [3.17] is as given in Figure 3.25.

$$m_1 rs\omega^2/I_A = \theta_0\{(cl^2\omega/I_A)^2 + (kl^2/I_A - \omega^2)^2\}^{0.5},$$

where

$$I_A = I_O + m_1 s^2.$$

Thus

$$\theta_0 = \frac{(m_1 rs\omega^2)/(I_O + m_1 s^2)}{[\{cl^2\omega/(I_O + m_1 s^2)\}^2 + \{kl^2/(I_O + m_1 s^2) - \omega^2\}^2]^{0.5}}.$$

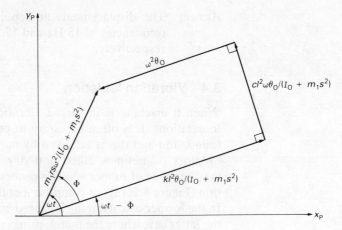

Figure 3.25   Phasor diagram for Example 3.6.

But

$$cl^2/(I_O + m_1s^2) = 2\xi\omega_n \quad \text{and} \quad kl^2/(I_O + m_1s^2) = \omega_n^2.$$

Hence

$$\theta_0 = \frac{(m_1rs\omega^2)/(I_O + m_1s^2)}{\{(2\xi\omega\omega_n)^2 + (\omega_n^2 - \omega^2)^2\}^{0.5}}$$

and

$$\theta_0 = \frac{(m_1rs\omega^2)/\{(I_O + m_1s^2)\omega_n^2\}}{[(2\xi\omega/\omega_n)^2 + \{1 - (\omega/\omega_n)^2\}^2]^{0.5}}.$$

We can also show (see Figure 3.25) that:

$$\tan\Phi = (cl^2\omega)/\{kl^2 - (I_O + m_1s^2)\omega^2\}.$$

Hence

$$\tan\Phi = 2\xi(\omega/\omega_n)/\{1 - (\omega/\omega_n)^2\}.$$

Numerical calculations lead to:

$$I_O = (7.8 \times 10^3 \times 0.6 \times 0.153 \times 0.006)(0.6^2/3 + 0.006^2/12)$$
$$= 0.51556 \text{ kg m}^2.$$

Thus

$$\theta_0 = \frac{(1.0 \times 10^{-3} \times 0.44)(\omega/\omega_n)^2/(0.51556 + 1.6 \times 0.44^2)}{[\{1 - (\omega/\omega_n)^2\}^2 + 4 \times 0.05^2(\omega/\omega_n)^2]^{0.5}}.$$

When

$$f = 15 \text{ Hz}, \quad \omega/\omega_n = 15/15.5 = 0.96774.$$

And $\theta_0 = 4.3140 \times 10^{-3}$ rad and displacement at a point 300 mm from the pivot is $0.3 \times 4.3140 \times 10^{-3} = 1.29$ mm. When $f = 15.5$ Hz, $\omega/\omega_n = 1$ and $\theta_0 = 5.3313 \times 10^{-3}$ rad and the required displacement is 1.60 mm.

Answer The displacements at a point 300 mm from the pivot for frequencies of 15 Hz and 15.5 Hz are **1.29 mm** and **1.60 mm,** respectively.

3.4 Vibration isolation

When a machine is in forced vibrations a force is transmitted to its foundations. It is often necessary to provide vibration isolation for the foundation and this is achieved by mounting the machine on vibration isolators (sometimes called anti-vibration mounts). These mountings may be made of rubber which is generally subjected to a shear deformation (Figure 3.26(a)) or comprise metal helical springs (Figure 3.26(b)). In the former case damping is caused by the rubber and is greater than in the latter case where the metal springs provide the damping.

We will assume that the vibration isolator provides a stiffness that is constant as well as damping that is equivalent to viscous damping. Thus, if the machine has only one degree of freedom, the situation is equivalent to that of Figure 3.1(a), where the isolators (typically there are four) provide a stiffness of k and a damping constant of c. Both the force in the spring and the force in the damper contribute to the force in the foundation. There is a phase difference of 90° between the damping force and the spring force, as shown in Figure 3.27. Let the amplitude of the force transmitted to the foundation be F_t, thus:

$$F_t = \{(kY)^2 + (c\omega Y)^2\}^{0.5},$$

where Y is the amplitude of the displacement of the machine of mass m and ω is the excitation frequency.

We now define a transmission ratio or transmissibility (TR):

$$TR = \frac{\text{amplitude of transmitted force}}{\text{amplitude of excitation force}}$$

$$= \{(kY)^2 + (c\omega Y)^2\}^{0.5}/F_0.$$

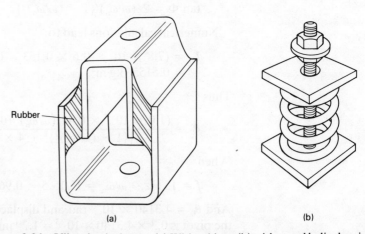

Rubber

(a)

(b)

Figure 3.26 Vibration isolators. (a) With rubber; (b) with metal helical springs.

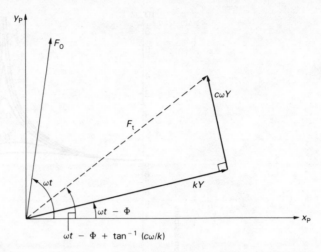

Figure 3.27   Phasor diagram showing force transmitted to foundations.

By making use of equation [3.7], we find that

$$TR = \frac{\{1 + (2\xi\omega/\omega_n)^2\}^{0.5}}{[\{1 - (\omega/\omega_n)^2\}^2 + \{2\xi\omega/\omega_n\}^2]^{0.5}}.$$ [3.18]

The values of transmissibility TR for different damping ratios plotted against ω/ω_n are shown in Figure 3.28. For ω/ω_n less than 1.414 the transmitted force is greater than the excitation force and there is no isolation. If ω/ω_n is greater than 1.414, then the transmission ratio is less than one. For good vibration isolation we require a high value of ω/ω_n and a low damping ratio.

Note that the equation [3.18] for transmission ratio is the same both for a constant amplitude excitation force, $F(t) = F_0 \sin \omega t$ and for an excitation force proportional to ω^2, $F(t) = m_1 r \omega^2 \sin \omega t$.

Example 3.7
Machine supported on vibration isolators

A machine is of total mass 2 tonnes and operates at 240 strokes per minute. The excitation force is equivalent to a force induced by an out-of-balance mass of 12 kg rotating at a radius of 100 mm.

The machine is to be mounted on four vibration isolators with negligible damping. For (1) $\omega/\omega_n = 2$ and (2) $\omega/\omega_n = 4$ determine:
  (a)   the static deflection of the machine,
  (b)   the transmission ratio,
  (c)   the stiffness of each isolator, and
  (d)   the amplitude of the displacement of the machine.

Given that the machine is directly attached to a concrete base of mass 6 tonnes, determine for this new case the four quantities listed above when $\omega/\omega_n = 2$.

Solution   (1) $\omega/\omega_n = 2$.

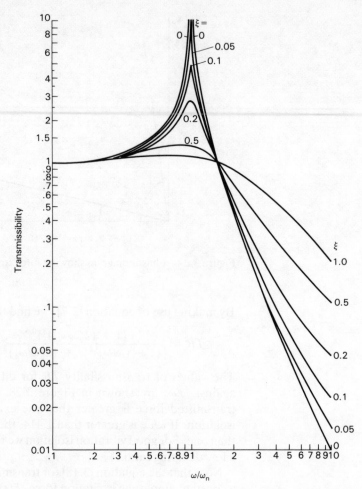

Figure 3.28 Transmissibility plotted against non-dimensional frequency ω/ω_n for different damping ratios ξ.

Frequency of the forced vibration of the machine is $240/60 = 4$ Hz. Undamped natural frequency $f_n = 2$ Hz, as $f/f_n = 2$ ($\omega/\omega_n = 2$).

Hence

$\omega_n = 2\pi \times 2 = 4\pi$ rad/s.

$\omega_n^2 = k/m$, where k is the equivalent stiffness of the four mounts. But $ky_0 = mg$, where y_0 is the static deflection and m the mass of the machine.

Hence

$y_0 = 9.81/(4\pi)^2 = 0.062$ m   or   62 mm.

We note that the static deflection y_0 depends upon the undamped circular natural frequency or, for a given ratio of ω/ω_n, the frequency of the forced vibration of the machine. The transmission ratio may be obtained either from equation [3.18] or from Figure 3.28, and for $\omega/\omega_n = 2$ its value is 0.333. The stiffness of the mounts is given by $k = m\omega_n^2$. Thus

$$k = 2000(4\pi)^2 = 315.8 \text{ kN/m}$$

and the stiffness of each isolator or mount is $315.8/4 = 78.95$ kN/m. The amplitude of displacement is obtained from equation [3.15] and for the damping ratio $\xi = 0$, we have

$$Y^2 = \{m_1 r(\omega/\omega_n)^2/m\}^2/\{1 - (\omega/\omega_n)^2\}^2.$$

For $\omega/\omega_n = 2$,

$$Y^2 = (12 \times 0.1 \times 2^2/2000)^2/(1 - 2^2)^2.$$

And

$$Y^2 = +0.80^2 \text{ mm} \qquad \text{and} \qquad Y = 0.80 \text{ mm}.$$

Answers to part (1)   (a)   Static deflection is **62 mm,**
                    (b)   transmission ratio is **0.33,**
                    (c)   stiffness of each isolator is **79 kN/m,**
                    (d)   displacement amplitude is **0.80 mm.**

$$(2) \quad \omega/\omega_n = 4.$$

We repeat the above calculations:
The undamped natural frequency is now 1 Hz.
Static deflection $y_0 = 9.81/(2\pi)^2 = 248$ mm.
Transmission ratio is 0.0667.
Stiffness of four isolators is $2000(2\pi)^2 = 78.96$ kN/m and each isolator has a stiffness of 19.74 kN/m.

$$Y^2 = (12 \times 0.1 \times 4^2/2000)^2/(1 - 4^2)^2.$$

Hence displacement amplitude $Y = 0.64$ mm.

Answers to part (2)   (a)   Static deflection is **248 mm,**
                    (b)   transmission ratio is **0.067,**
                    (c)   stiffness of each isolator is **19.7 kN/m,**
                    (d)   displacement amplitude is **0.64 mm.**

Some interesting points arise out of this example. The vibration isolation discussed in part (2) is very good, but the static deflection compared with that in part (1) has been increased by a factor of four and the mount stiffness reduced by the same factor. Thus good isolation is achieved at the expense of a high static deflection. In our example a static deflection of 248 mm is hardly practicable and would mean mounting the machine on very soft springs. If really good isolation is required, then either air springs or active isolation has to be employed.

The example also shows that the displacement amplitude is not reduced much by improving the vibration isolation. In applications where pipes conveying compressed air or water are attached to the machine a displacement of 0.64 mm may be too great. The final part of this question shows how the amplitude of the displacement of the vibrating machine can be reduced.

With the machine on a concrete base the total mass of the system becomes 8000 kg. The undamped natural circular frequency remains 4π rad/s. The static deflection is independent of mass and retains the value of 62 mm. The transmission ratio is also unchanged at 0.333.

Stiffness of the mounts $= 8000(4\pi)^2 = 1263.3$ kN/m and the stiffness of each isolator is 315.8 kN/m. For the displacement amplitude,

$$Y^2 = (12 \times 0.1 \times 2^2/8000)^2/(1 - 2^2)^2.$$

Hence

$$Y = 0.2 \text{ mm}.$$

The important point to note here is that by increasing the mass that is vibrating by a factor of four we have reduced the amplitude of the displacement for the vibration by a factor of four to 0.20 mm, a level which may be more acceptable. Besides reducing the vibration the new system with the concrete base will have a lower centre of mass and hence will be more stable. It should be less likely to have a rotational vibration (which would mean an extra degree of freedom) and the transient effects of any starting torques would be less.

Example 3.8
Couple transmitted to foundations

In Figure 3.29 is shown a rigid link AGB which is pivoted to the foundation by a pin at G. The centre of mass of the link is at G and the moment of inertia about an axis through G, perpendicular to the plane of motion, is I_G. A damper of rate C and a spring of stiffness k are pinned to the link at A and B as shown.

A couple has a moment Q which varies sinusoidally with time. The moment has an amplitude Q_0 and circular frequency ω. The couple is applied to the link and gives rise to a steady-state angular oscillation of the link.

Assuming that the amplitude of this oscillation is small, and neglecting the effects of gravity and the masses of the spring and dashpot, show that:

(a) there is no net force transmitted to the foundations,

(b) the net couple transmitted to the foundations has a moment with amplitude of

$$Q_0[\{k^2l_2^4 + C^2l_1^4\omega^2\}/\{((kl_2^2 - I_G\omega^2) + C^2l_1^4\omega^2\}]^{0.5}.$$

Solution When the link AGB is displaced through a small angle θ the free-body diagram for the link is as shown in Figure 3.30.

(a) The force acting on the link at the pivot has the components R_H and R_V in the horizontal and vertical directions, respectively (see Figure 3.30). The centre of mass of the link AGB coincides with the pivot and thus G has no acceleration. Considering force components in the horizontal and vertical directions, respectively, we obtain:

$$R_H = kl_2\theta \quad \text{and} \quad R_V = Cl_1\dot{\theta}.$$

The forces on the foundations are shown in Figure 3.31 and it can be seen

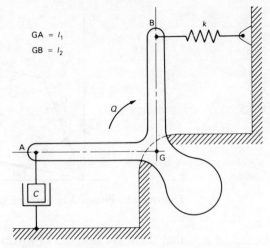

GA = l_1

GB = l_2

Figure 3.29   Diagram for Example 3.8.

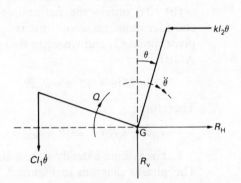

Figure 3.30   Free-body diagram for Example 3.8.

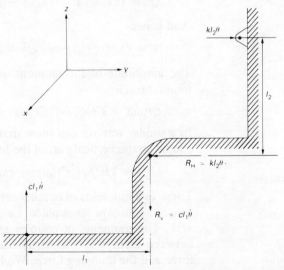

Figure 3.31   Diagram showing forces on the foundation for Example 3.8.

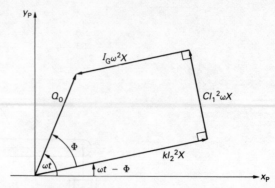

Figure 3.32 Phasor diagram for Example 3.8.

that there are two sets of forces with the same magnitude, opposite in sense and separated by distances l_1 or l_2. These two sets of forces form two couples and the resultant force on the foundations is zero.

(b) To obtain the net couple transmitted to the foundations we consider moments about the axis, perpendicular to AGB, through the pivot, point G, and we write down the equation of motion for the link AGB:

$$Q - kl_2^2\theta - Cl_1^2\dot{\theta} = I_G\ddot{\theta}.$$

Therefore,

$$I_G\ddot{\theta} + Cl_1^2\dot{\theta} + kl_2^2\theta = Q_0 \sin \omega t.$$

Let us assume a steady-state solution of the form $\theta = X \sin (\omega t - \Phi)$. The phasor diagram in Figure 3.32 can be constructed to obtain the amplitude X.

From the phasor diagram an expression involving X may be obtained:

$$Q_0^2 = (Cl_1^2\omega X)^2 + (kl_2^2 X - I_G\omega^2 X)^2.$$

And hence

$$X = Q_0/\{(Cl_1^2\omega)^2 + (kl_2^2 - I_G\omega^2)^2\}^{0.5}.$$

The amplitude of the moment of the couple acting on the horizontal foundations is:

$$Cl_1^2\omega X = Cl_1^2 Q_0\omega/\{(Cl_1^2\omega)^2 + (kl_2^2 - I_G\omega^2)^2\}^{0.5}.$$

In a similar way we can show that the amplitude of the moment of the couple on the vertical part of the foundation is:

$$kl_2^2 X = kl_2^2 Q_0/\{(Cl_1^2\omega)^2 + (kl_2^2 - I_G\omega^2)^2\}^{0.5}.$$

These two moments of couples are vectors perpendicular to the plane in which the motion takes place, i.e., the vectors in x direction, see Figure 3.31. The moments of couples are also phasors and the phase angle between them is 90°, which is also the phase angle between the spring force and the damping force. We have to take this phase difference into account to obtain the moment of the net couple to the foundations. Using

Pythagoras's theorem we obtain the amplitude of the moment of the couple.

$$Q_0[(k^2l_2^4 + C^2l_1^4\omega^2)/\{(kl_2^2 - I_G\omega^2)^2 + C^2l_1^4\omega^2\}]^{0.5}.$$

**Example 3.9
Selection of vibration
isolators**

A single-cylinder, reciprocating compressor of mass 500 kg is to run at 1500 rev/min, and is to be mounted on four vibration isolators. Two catalogues are available from which the isolators are to be selected. In the first the isolators are based on rubber and in the second on metallic springs. See Figure 3.26 for diagrams of the two kinds. There are five isolators of different sizes in each catalogue, and from the information given the stiffnesses k and damping constants c are estimated to be as shown in Table 3.1.

Table 3.1

	Catalogue 1 (rubber)		Catalogue 2 (metal)	
	k (kN/m)	c (N s/m)	k (kN/m)	c (N s/m)
1	250	2000	75	110
2	500	1800	150	115
3	1000	1500	250	140
4	1800	1000	500	160
5	2500	500	750	200

The compressor on the isolators form a system with a single degree of freedom, for which the appropriate transmissibility curves are shown in Figure 3.28.

(a) Select a set of suitable isolators and give reasons for your choice.

(b) If the compressor were to be bolted directly to a bedplate of mass 1 tonne what isolators would you now select? With the bedplate and the new isolators would the amplitude of the displacement of the resulting vibration be less than in (a)? Estimate the ratio of the new displacement amplitude to that in (a).

Each isolator is designed to take a maximum load of 500 kg.

Note that the data in the table above refers to a single isolator, whereas four are required to support the machine.

Solution (a) The circular frequency of the likely main vibration corresponds to the running speed of the compressor and is

$2\pi \times 1500/60 = 157.1$ rad/s.

For each value of isolator stiffness the undamped circular natural frequency ω_n of the system, the damping ratio ξ and the static deflection y_0 can be obtained from the following formulae:

$$\omega_n = (4k/m)^{0.5}, \qquad \xi = 4c/(2m\omega_n) \qquad \text{and} \qquad y_0 = mg/(4k),$$

where m is the mass of the compressor. Table 3.2 gives the data.

Table 3.2

	Catalogue 1 (rubber)				Catalogue 2 (metal)			
	ω_n	ω/ω_n	ξ	y_0 (mm)	ω_n	ω/ω_n	ξ	y_0 (mm)
1	44.7	3.51	0.179	4.9	24.5	6.41	0.016	16.4
2	63.2	2.49	0.114	2.5	34.6	4.54	0.013	8.2
3	89.4	1.76	0.067	1.2	44.7	3.51	0.013	4.9
4	120.0	1.31	0.033	0.7	63.2	2.49	0.010	2.5
5	141.4	1.11	0.014	0.5	77.5	2.03	0.010	1.6

Transmissibility corresponding to $\omega/\omega_n = 2$ is normally adequate for most machines. For a reciprocating compressor, however, a lower value of transmissibility is normally required and hence the choice $\omega/\omega_n = 3$ is more appropriate. Let us consider $\omega/\omega_n = 3.51$. Catalogue 2 (isolator no. 3) gives lower TR value than catalogue 1 (isolator no. 1), because the damping ratio is less. On the other hand catalogue 2 isolators will cost more. Static deflection y_0 is quite acceptable.

Taking all these arguments into account we choose isolator no. 3 from catalogue 2.

(b)   With the bedplate the mass m is now 1500 kg. New values for ω_n, etc., are shown in Table 3.3.

Let us choose isolator 5 from catalogue 2, for which $\omega/\omega_n = 3.51$, or isolator no. 3 from catalogue 1, where $\omega/\omega_n = 3.04$. Either would be acceptable. Let us choose the one from catalogue 2 to be consistent with the selection carried out in part (a) of the example.

Next we consider the displacement amplitudes. Amplitude Y is given by:

$$Y/(m_1 r/m) = (\omega/\omega_n)^2/[\{1 - (\omega/\omega_n)^2\}^2 + (2\xi\omega/\omega_n)^2]^{0.5},$$

where $m_1 r$ is a constant and ξ is too small to have a significant effect on the estimate.

Thus

$$Y \propto (1/m)(\omega/\omega_n)^2/\{1 - (\omega/\omega_n)^2\}.$$

With the isolators selected the ratio ω/ω_n is 3.51 in both cases. With the bedplate the amplitude of the displacement of the compressor is reduced by a factor of 500/1500 or 1/3.

Table 3.3

	Catalogue 1				Catalogue 2			
	ω_n	ω/ω_n	ξ	y_0 (mm)	ω_n	ω/ω_n	ξ	y_0 (mm)
1	25.8	6.09	0.103	14.7	14.1	11.14	0.0095	49.1
2	36.5	4.30	0.066	7.4	20.0	7.86	0.0077	24.5
3	51.6	3.04	0.039	3.7	25.8	6.09	0.0072	14.7
4	69.3	2.27	0.019	2.0	36.5	4.30	0.0058	7.4
5	81.6	1.93	0.008	1.5	44.7	3.51	0.0060	4.9

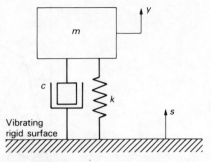

Figure 3.33   System with a single degree of freedom, with base excitation.

3.5   Base excitation

Forced vibrations are not necessarily excited by a force directly applied to a body, but may occur because the single degree of freedom system is attached to a surface which is itself vibrating. A possible situation is shown in Figure 3.33 where the spring and damper are attached to a rigid surface which itself has a displacement. A car passing over a bumpy road is subjected to this kind of excitation. Delicate measuring instruments, which have to be protected from vibration, may be supported on the body of mass m, as in Figure 3.33. We will also show that the model shown in Figure 3.33 can represent certain vibration measuring instruments.

It is shown in Figure 3.33 that the displacement s of the rigid base surface to which the single degree of freedom system is attached causes the rigid body of mass m to be displaced by y. Both displacements are specified in the same co-ordinate system, therefore the extension of the spring is $y - s$. The free-body diagram for this rigid body of mass m is shown in Figure 3.34. The equation of motion for the body is:

$$-c(\dot{y} - \dot{s}) - k(y - s) = m\ddot{y}.$$

At this stage we introduce a new variable z, such that $z = y - s$. Thus

$$m\ddot{z} + c\dot{z} + kz = -m\ddot{s}$$

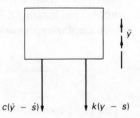

Figure 3.34   Free-body diagram for system shown in Figure 3.33.

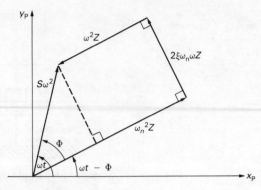

Figure 3.35   Phasor diagram for system with base excitation.

or

$$\ddot{z} + 2\xi\omega_n\dot{z} + \omega_n^2 z = -\ddot{s},$$

where ξ is the damping ratio and ω_n the undamped circular natural frequency. Let us assume that the base displacement is sinusoidal in time, with circular frequency ω and amplitude S. So $s = S \sin \omega t$, and

$$\ddot{z} + 2\xi\omega_n\dot{z} + \omega_n^2 z = \omega^2 S \sin \omega t. \qquad [3.19]$$

The steady-state solution of differential equation [3.19] is of the form

$$z = Z \sin (\omega t - \Phi),$$

where Z is the amplitude and Φ the phase angle. The phasor diagram corresponding to equation [3.19] is shown in Figure 3.35. From the phasor diagram one obtains:

$$(S\omega^2)^2 = (\omega_n^2 Z - \omega^2 Z)^2 + (2\xi\omega\omega_n Z)^2.$$

And

$$Z/S = (\omega/\omega_n)^2/[\{1 - (\omega/\omega_n)^2\}^2 + (2\xi\omega/\omega_n)^2]^{0.5}, \qquad [3.20]$$

$$\tan \Phi = (2\xi\omega/\omega_n)/\{1 - (\omega/\omega_n)^2\}.$$

The relations between the ratio Z/S and the non-dimensional frequency ω/ω_n give curves with the same shape as those of Figure 3.19 which shows the forced-vibration response caused by a rotating out-of-balance mass. The ordinate $Y/(m_1 r/m)$ in Figure 3.19 is replaced by Z/S. Equation [3.20] provides a theoretical background to some vibration measuring instruments (see Example 3.11).

A similar expression may be obtained relating Y and S:

$$\frac{Y}{S} = \frac{\{1 + (2\xi\omega/\omega_n)^2\}^{0.5}}{[\{1 - (\omega/\omega_n)^2\}^2 + (2\xi\omega/\omega_n)^2]^{0.5}}. \qquad [3.21]$$

The right-hand side of equation [3.21] is the same as the right-hand side of equation [3.18] in the expression for the transmission ratio. Thus if a delicate instrument is placed on a metrological table, resting on ground which is vibrating with an amplitude S and frequency ω, then in order to maintain amplitude Y as small as possible the same principles apply as for effective vibration isolation. To obtain effective isolation the amplitude of the force transmitted to the foundations should be reduced. This is achieved by ensuring that the ratio ω/ω_n is 2 or more and that the damping ratio is as low as possible.

Example 3.10
Beam with forced displacement at one end

Figure 3.36 shows a rigid link BCD which can pivot about the axis through C and has a moment of inertia about this axis of 0.25 kg m^2. The spring AB has a stiffness of 700 N/m and the damper DE has a rate of 60 N per m/s; both spring and damper may be assumed to be massless.

The forced displacement y of end A of the spring is sinusoidal with a circular frequency of 10 rad/s and an amplitude of 1 cm.

Find the amplitude of angular displacement, assuming this to be small, of the steady-state forced oscillation of link BCD.

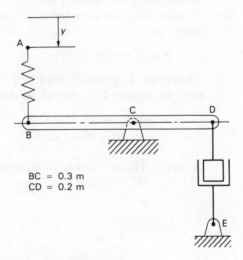

Figure 3.36   Diagram for Example 3.10.

Solution   The extension of the spring AB is $(0.3\theta - y)$ [m], if it is assumed that A is displaced downwards and the displacement of B is greater than that of A. The angle θ is the small, angular anti-clockwise displacement of the link or beam BCD. (If we assume the displacement of A downwards to be greater than that of B, the compression of the spring becomes $(y - 0.3\theta)$ and the spring force is reversed in sense. The final result is the same.)

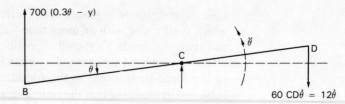

Figure 3.37   Free-body diagram for Example 3.10.

The free-body diagram for the link is shown in Figure 3.37. Considering moments about the fixed rotation axis through C, we obtain the equation of motion for the link:

$$-0.2 \times 12\dot{\theta} - 0.3 \times 700(0.3\theta - y) = 0.25\ddot{\theta}$$

or

$$0.25\ddot{\theta} + 2.4\dot{\theta} + 63\theta = 210y$$

or

$$\ddot{\theta} + 9.6\dot{\theta} + 252\theta = 840y. \qquad [3.22]$$

Additionally we know that $y = 0.01 \sin \omega t$ [m], where ω is 10 rad/s. Therefore we can write the steady-state solution of equation [3.22] in the form:

$$\theta = X \sin (10t - \Phi).$$

The phasor diagram for equation [3.22] is given in Figure 3.38. Therefore from the phasor diagram one obtains:

$$X = 8.4/\{96^2 + 152^2\}^{0.5}$$
$$= 0.0467 \text{ rad (or } 2.68°).$$

Answer   The amplitude of steady-state forced oscillations of the link BCD is **2.68°**.

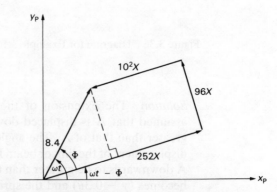

Figure 3.38   Phasor diagram for Example 3.10.

**Example 3.11
Principles of an
accelerometer**

Outline the operating principles of an accelerometer. Sketch and describe a commercial accelerometer that uses piezo-electric material.

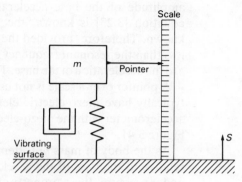

Figure 3.39   Principle of an accelerometer.

Solution Let us consider a body of mass m attached to a vibrating surface through a spring and damper, as shown in Figure 3.39. Let us assume that the vibrating surface or base has a displacement of amplitude S and an acceleration amplitude $S\omega^2$ which we are trying to measure. A scale is attached to the base and moves with it. A pointer is rigidly attached to the mass and moves over the scale. Thus the pointer, as it moves over the scale, will indicate the relative displacement z (with amplitude Z) of the body relative to the base. From equation [3.20] we may write:

$$Z/(S\omega^2) = (1/\omega_n^2)/[\{1 - (\omega/\omega_n)^2\}^2 + (2\xi\omega/\omega_n)^2]^{0.5}. \qquad [3.23]$$

A sketch of $Z/(S\omega^2)$ against ω/ω_n for different damping ratios is shown in Figure 3.40. These curves are very similar to those of Figure 3.5(a). In the region where ω is small compared with ω_n the ratio $Z/(S\omega^2)$ is almost

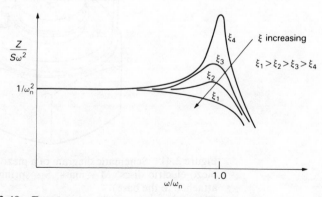

Figure 3.40   Frequency response curves for accelerometers.

constant and independent of frequency and damping ratio. In this region the amplitude of the relative displacement Z is proportional to the acceleration amplitude of the base. In general we may say that the instantaneous displacement z is proportional to the acceleration of the base. If we can measure Z we can obtain a quantity proportional to the amplitude of the base acceleration, and once the right-hand side of equation [3.23] is known, the amplitude of the base acceleration is known. Therefore, provided the frequencies of base vibration are much less than the resonant frequency, a single constant may be used to relate z to the acceleration of the base. This is the principle of the accelerometer.

A pointer over a scale is not used in commercial accelerometers which typically have piezo-electric elements. A centre-mounted mass–spring accelerometer with the piezo-electric material in compression is shown in Figure 3.41.

As the body of mass m (often referred to as a seismic mass) vibrates relative to the base of the accelerometer, the piezo-electric discs come under pressure. It is a property of piezo-electric materials that when they are under changing pressure in this way, an output voltage is self-generated by the material. This output voltage is proportional to z (and is equivalent to the pointer displacement on the scale as shown in Figure 3.39). The output voltage can be amplified and its magnitude presented as an r.m.s. value on a meter or as an instantaneous acceleration signal against time on an oscilloscope.

Quartz could be used as the piezo-electric material. Quartz crystal is a very stable material, but it needs a large change in pressure to be applied to produce a reasonable voltage output; thus accelerometers which use quartz are of low sensitivity. More often a material like lead zirconate titanate is employed. This is piezo-electric only when impurities are added; it is much more sensitive than quartz.

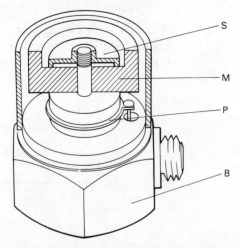

Figure 3.41 Schematic diagram of a piezo-electric accelerometer. B – base, P – piezo-electric discs, M – mass, S – spring (screwed to a centre post which is attached to the base).
(Diagram courtesy of Brüel and Kjær, Denmark.)

In a commercial accelerometer it is not usual to include damping. The resonant frequency is generally very high (up to 200 kHz) for small devices, and the operating range covers frequencies up to about 0.3 of the resonant frequency.

Example 3.12
Amplitude and phase errors of an accelerometer

An accelerometer has an undamped natural frequency of vibration f_n of 120 kHz. The base of the accelerometer is subjected to a sinusoidal acceleration of constant amplitude. The accelerometer is used at different frequencies.

If the accelerometer is used at $f = 60$ kHz, what will be the % error in the acceleration reading compared with that at 0 Hz? What will be the error in phase at 60 kHz? Carry out these calculations for damping ratios of (a) $\xi = 0$ and (b) $\xi = 0.2$.

Solution *Amplitude errors*
(a) $\xi = 0$
When the value of f approaches zero, one obtains from equation [3.23]:

$$Z/(S\omega^2)|_{f=0} = 1/\omega_n^2.$$

When $f = 60$ kHz, $f/f_n = 0.5$, and for this case:

$$Z/(S\omega^2)|_{f=60} = (1/\omega_n^2)/(1 - 0.5^2) = 1.333/\omega_n^2.$$

$S\omega^2$ is the amplitude of the acceleration and is assumed constant at different frequencies of base oscillations. Thus the accelerometer indicates an acceleration 33% greater than at low frequencies.

(b) $\xi = 0.2$
When $f/f_n = 0.5$

$$\begin{aligned} Z/(S\omega^2)|_{f=60} &= (1/\omega_n^2)/\{(1 - 0.5^2)^2 + (2 \times 0.2 \times 0.5)^2\}^{0.5} \\ &= (1/\omega_n^2)/(0.75^2 + 0.2^2)^{0.5} \\ &= 1.288/\omega_n^2. \end{aligned}$$

The error is now 29%.

Phase errors
If the phase angle of s, the displacement of the base of the accelerometer, in relation to the relative displacement z is Φ, then the phase angle of acceleration $\ddot{s}$ in relation to the relative displacement is $\Phi + \pi$. See Figure 3.35. Thus

$$\tan(\Phi + \pi) = \tan \Phi = (2\xi\omega/\omega_n)/\{1 - (\omega/\omega_n)^2\}.$$

(a) $\xi = 0$
If there is no damping there is no error in phase angle reading for $f = 60$ kHz in comparison with that at 0 Hz. The phase angle Φ between the displacement of the base and the relative displacement z is in this case always equal to zero.

(b) $\xi = 0.2$

When $f/f_n = 0.5$

$$\tan \Phi = (2 \times 0.2 \times 0.5)/(1 - 0.5^2) = 0.2/0.75 = 0.2667.$$

Hence $\Phi = 14.93°$.

Answers $\xi = 0$, amplitude error is **33%**, phase error is **0°**.
$\xi = 0.2$, amplitude error is **29%**, phase error is **14.93°**.

Example 3.13
Principles of a
vibrometer

Outline the operating principles of a vibrometer for measuring the displacement of a vibrating surface.

Solution   A vibrometer comprises a spring–mass–damper system attached to the vibrating surface whose displacement is to be measured, as shown in Figure 3.33. From equation [3.20] we may write:

$$Z/S = 1/[\{1/(\omega/\omega_n)^2 - 1\}^2 + \{2\xi/(\omega/\omega_n)\}^2]^{0.5}.$$

When $\omega/\omega_n \gg 1$, $Z/S = 1$. In this case the amplitude of the relative displacement is equal to the amplitude of the vibrating surface or base. If we consider the system with a pointer and scale, as shown in Figure 3.39, then the pointer on the scale is indicating the displacement of the base surface, providing the frequency of the base is well above that of the natural frequency. The phase difference between z and s is 180°, and the body of mass m has no displacement with respect to a co-ordinate system fixed in space.

The important distinction between an accelerometer and a vibrometer is that the latter is an instrument with a low natural frequency which is used to measure displacements of vibrating surfaces at frequencies well above its natural frequency, whereas an accelerometer has a high natural frequency and is used to measure acceleration of vibrating surfaces at lower frequencies.

Example 3.14
Measuring instrument
with pivoted crank

An instrument for measuring small amplitudes of displacement of a vibratory surface is shown in Figure 3.42. The instrument comprises a light crank BOC, which is pivoted to the casing at O. A small body of mass 0.5 kg is fixed to the crank at C and a dashpot D and spring E are attached as shown. A pointer moves over a scale scribed on the casing. The instrument is not yet calibrated to read directly the amplitude of the displacement of the base. The damping ratio of the instrument is 0.6 and the undamped natural frequency is 2.5 Hz.

(a)   Determine the damping constant of the dashpot D and the stiffness of the spring E.

(b)   Given that the amplitude indicated by the pointer is 0.5 mm when the frequency of vibration of the surface to which the instrument is attached is 2 Hz, find the amplitude of the displacement of the surface.

(c) What is the percentage error in the reading at 2 Hz?

Note that angle BOC is a right angle, and in the equilibrium position OC is horizontal.

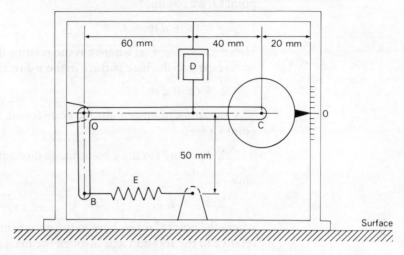

Figure 3.42 Diagram for Example 3.14.

Solution (a) To answer the first part of the problem we could regard the base surface as stationary in space, so that the axis through point O is fixed in space and consider only free, damped vibrations of the system. However, we will choose a more general approach to solve this problem, because in parts (b) and (c) of the question the instrument case is assumed to be vibrating.

When the crank BOC is deflected through a small angle θ in the anti-clockwise sense the free-body diagram for the crank is as shown in Figure 3.43. Note that in this diagram the weight is not shown, as the

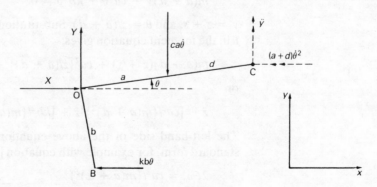

Figure 3.43 Free-body diagram for Example 3.14.

moment of the weight in the static equilibrium position of the system cancels out with the moment of the spring force at static equilibrium. In the fixed (absolute) co-ordinate system xy, shown in Figure 3.43, the acceleration components of the point mass m, situated at the point C, are $-(a + d)\dot\theta^2$ and $\ddot y$ in the x and y directions, respectively. Assuming that s is the displacement of the base surface, as well as the displacement of the point O, we obtain:

$$y = (a + d)\theta + s.$$

However, $y = z + s$, where z is the relative displacement of the point C with respect to the base surface in the y direction. Thus:

$$z = (a + d)\theta.$$

The equations of motion for the body (crank BOC and small body at the point C) are:

$$\Sigma F_y = m\ddot y \quad \text{(in the } y \text{ co-ordinate direction)}$$

and

$$\Sigma M_C = I_C\ddot\theta,$$

where the point C refers here to the mass centre. Moments M_C are taken relative to the rotation axis through the mass centre. I_C denotes here the moment of inertia in relation to the same axis. Hence the two equations of motion give:

$$Y - ca\dot\theta = m\ddot y \tag{3.24}$$

and

$$Y(a + d) - cad\dot\theta + kb^2\theta = 0, \tag{3.25}$$

where c and k are the damping constant and stiffness, respectively. By substituting Y from equation [3.24] in [3.25] we obtain:

$$(m\ddot y + ca\dot\theta)(a + d) - cad\dot\theta + kb^2\theta = 0$$

or

$$m(a + d)\ddot y + ca^2\dot\theta + kb^2\theta = 0.$$

$y = z + s$, and $\theta = z/(a + d)$. Substitution of these expressions for y and θ in the moment equation gives:

$$m(a + d)(\ddot z + \ddot s) + ca^2\{\dot z/(a + d)\} + kb^2\{z/(a + d)\} = 0$$

or

$$\ddot z + [ca^2/\{m(a + d)^2\}]\dot z + [kb^2/\{m(a + d)^2\}]z = -\ddot s. \tag{3.26}$$

The left-hand side of the above equation may be compared with the standard form, for example with equation [2.3]. Hence

$$2\xi\omega_n = ca^2/\{m(a + d)^2\}$$

and

$$\omega_n^2 = kb^2/\{m(a + d)^2\}.$$

Finally, we know from the text of the question that damping ratio $\xi = 0.6$, and the undamped circular natural frequency $\omega_n = 2\pi \times 2.5$ rad/s. Also $a = 60\,\text{mm}$, $d = 40\,\text{mm}$, $b = 50\,\text{mm}$ and $m = 0.5\,\text{kg}$. Hence,

$$c \times 0.06^2/(0.5 \times 0.1^2) = 2 \times 0.6 \times 5\pi$$

and

$$k \times 0.05^2/(0.5 \times 0.1^2) = (5\pi)^2.$$

Therefore

$$c = 26.18\,\text{N s/m} \qquad \text{and} \qquad k = 493.5\,\text{N/m}.$$

Answer to part (a)   Damping constant of the dashpot is **26.18 N s/m** and the stiffness of the spring is **493.5 N/m.**

In this problem we may obtain c and k more simply by considering only free, damped vibrations and regarding the rotation axis through point O as an axis fixed in space. In this case the base surface is also fixed. Hence the equation describing rotation of the system (light crank BOC and small body at C) about the fixed axis through point O is

$$\Sigma M_O = I_O \ddot{\theta},$$

where I_O is the moment of inertia of the small body (point mass at C) in relation to the fixed axis through O and:

$$I_O = m(a + d)^2.$$

Hence

$$-ca^2\dot{\theta} - kb^2\theta = m(a + d)^2\ddot{\theta}.$$

Thus

$$m(a + d)^2\ddot{\theta} + ca^2\dot{\theta} + kb^2\theta = 0.$$

Finally, by comparing this equation with its standard form (equation [2.3]) we will obtain the values for c and k.

(b)   By using the first method to solve part (a) of the example we are able to find directly the answer to the second part of the question, (b). The displacement of the oscillating base surface is:

$$s = S \sin \omega t,$$

where $\omega = 2\pi \times 2$ and S is the amplitude.

The steady-state solution for equation [3.26] has the form:

$$z = Z \sin (\omega t - \Phi), \qquad \text{where} \qquad Z = (100/120) \times 0.5\,\text{mm}.$$

The ratio (100/120) results from the fact that the pointer is 120 mm from the pivot and that the body, having relative displacement z, is located at C, 100 mm from O. The phasor diagram of equation [3.26] for the steady-state solution is shown in Figure 3.44.

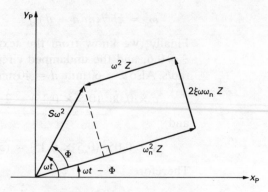

Figure 3.44 Phasor diagram for Example 3.14.

Hence

$$(S\omega^2)^2 = (\omega_n^2 Z - \omega^2 Z)^2 + (2\xi\omega\omega_n Z)^2.$$

Substituting for ω_n and ξ their numerical values, we obtain:

$$S = Z\{(18.85/\omega)^2 + (1 - 246.74/\omega^2)^2\}^{0.5}. \tag{3.27}$$

Hence

$$S = (0.5 \times 100/120) \times (1.602) = 0.6675 \text{ mm.}$$

Answer to part (b) Amplitude of the displacement of the surface is **0.67 mm.**

(c)   From equation [3.27] we can deduce that at very large values of ω the amplitude of the displacement of the body relative to the base is equal to the amplitude of the displacement of the base:

$$S = Z$$

If the base surface vibrates with the same displacement amplitude as at 2 Hz but with high frequency:

$$Z = S = 0.6675 \text{ mm.}$$

However, at 2 Hz the pointer indicated the amplitude of its relative displacement as 0.5 mm. Therefore, the amplitude of the relative displacement of the body was in this case:

$$0.5 \times 100/120 = 0.4167 \text{ mm.}$$

Hence the percentage error in the reading at 2 Hz amounts to

$$(0.6675 - 0.4167) \times 100/0.6675 = 37.6\%.$$

This error occurs because the instrument is being used below its natural frequency.

Answer to part (c) Error in measuring the surface displacement amplitude is **37.6%.**

Problems

3.1 A machine of mass 350 kg rests on supports with stiffness 160 kN/m and viscous damping 0.2 of the critical value. Part of the machine has a mass of 1 kg and moves vertically with simple harmonic motion of frequency 10 Hz and stroke 60 mm.

Calculate:

(a) the amplitude of forced vertical vibrations of the machine and the phase angle by which the displacement lags the excitation force,

(b) the magnitude of the vibratory force transmitted to the foundations and its phase angle relative to the applied force.

Answers (a) 0.096 mm, 171.3° (b) 23.8 N, 121.7°.

3.2 A bell crank lever is pivoted at O, as shown in Figure 3.45. The spring at A has a stiffness of 400 N/m and the viscous damper attached at B has a damping constant of 130 N s/m. The moment of inertia of the bell crank lever about an axis through O perpendicular to the *xy* plane is 0.1 kg m². In the equilibrium position OA is vertical. A sinusoidal force *F* of magnitude 50 N and frequency 3 Hz is applied horizontally at A. Calculate the amplitude of the resulting steady-state angular oscillations of the bell crank lever.

Answer 9.7°.

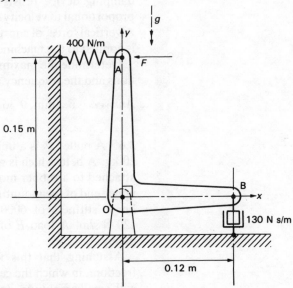

Figure 3.45 Diagram for Problem 3.2.

3.3 A machine of mass 1400 kg is supported on vibration isolators which together have a stiffness of 50 kN/m and provide a viscous damping constant of 0.2 of the critical value. The machine has one degree of freedom in the vertical direction.

Operation of the machine at a certain speed generates a sinusoidal force of constant amplitude F at a frequency of 0.95 Hz. At this speed of operation the amplitude of the vertical vibration of the machine is 5 mm.

Determine:

(a) the amplitude F of the exciting force,

(b) the amplitude of the vibratory force transmitted to the ground.

Answers (a) 100 N (b) 269 N.

3.4 A punching machine of mass 510 kg is supported by a mounting which has a stiffness of 240 kN/m and which exerts a viscous damping force of 9600 N at 1 m/s. Part of the machine of mass 8 kg executes simple harmonic motion and moves vertically through a stroke of 40 mm.

Calculate the amplitude of steady-state forced vibrations when the machine is running at 380 strokes/min.

Answer 0.37 mm.

3.5 A machine of mass 23 kg is mounted on four springs each of which deflects 0.05 mm when a force of 1 N is applied to it. A damping device resists the motion of the machine with a force proportional to velocity such that the force is equal to 150 N at 1 m/s. A vertical force, of constant amplitude 55 N and variable frequency, is applied to the machine.

Determine the maximum amplitude of steady-state forced vibrations and the frequency at which it occurs.

Answers 6.2 mm, 9.36 Hz.

3.6 A pulley A is a uniform cylinder of radius 200 mm and mass 20 kg. A belt, which is wrapped round the pulley, is fixed at B and attached to a rubber mounting at C, as shown in Figure 3.46. The upper end of the mounting is fixed at D. The rubber mounting has a linear stiffness of 6000 N/m and a linear damping constant of 120 N s/m. A load E of mass 30 kg hangs from the centre of the pulley A.

Assuming that this forms a system with a single degree of freedom, in which the centre of the pulley A can oscillate vertically with small amplitude, determine:

(a) the undamped circular natural frequency and the damping ratio of the system, and

(b) the amplitude of the displacement of the load for the steady-state vibrations when a couple with a moment of magnitude 6.0 sin $18t$ N m is applied to the pulley A about the axis of the pulley.

Answers (a) 20 rad/s, 0.2 (b) 3.1 mm.

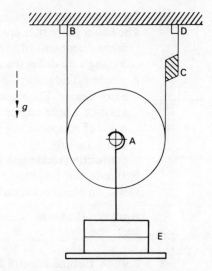

Figure 3.46   Diagram for Problem 3.6.

3.7   Two slender, uniform rods, AB and BC, each of mass 2 kg and length 0.5 m, are welded together so that their axes are at 60° to each other. The rods are pinned about a fixed point B and AB is held horizontally in static equilibrium by a spring at A of stiffness 30 kN/m, as shown in Figure 3.47.

A harmonic force of amplitude 20 N and frequency 20 Hz is applied vertically at C. Damping, characterized by a damping constant of 20 N s/m, is provided by a dashpot which is attached at C at right angles to BC.

For small steady-state oscillations of ABC determine:
(a)   the differential equation defining the oscillations,
(b)   the undamped circular natural frequency and the damping ratio,
(c)   the amplitude of the displacement of the point A.

Answers   (a) Approx. $\ddot{\theta} + 15\dot{\theta} + 22\,500\theta = 15 \sin 40\pi t$
(b) 150 rad/s, 0.05 (c) 1.07 mm.

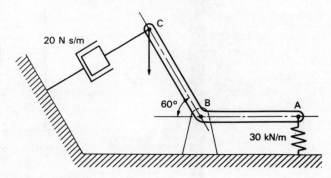

Figure 3.47   Diagram for Problem 3.7.

3.8 Two steel beams 5 m long are simply supported at each end. The beam properties are:

    second moment of area of each beam 20×10^6 mm^4,
    Young's modulus for steel   210 GPa.

A single-cylinder engine is mounted on a bedplate at the centre of the two beams. The engine details are:

    mass of whole engine and bedplate   180 kg,
    mass of reciprocating parts   2.2 kg,
    crank radius   63 mm,
    connecting rod length is large compared with crank radius.

Estimate the amplitude of the displacement for the steady-state vibration which occurs when the engine is running at 500 rev/min.

Answer 0.14 mm.

3.9 A turbine control linkage is shown in Figure 3.48. A is the control valve cylinder and BGD is a lever of mass 18 kg and radius of gyration about G of 200 mm. D is a fixed pivot point. A light spring S of stiffness 2500 N/m is attached at B and the other end of the spring is given a continuous simple harmonic motion of amplitude 5 mm and frequency 4 Hz. The mass of the control valve and piston is 12 kg. The force resisting the motion of the piston is proportional to velocity and is equal to 175 N at 1 m/s.

Determine the amplitude of motion of the piston in the cylinder and the maximum force acting on the pin at G.

Answers 4.62 mm, 40.4 N.

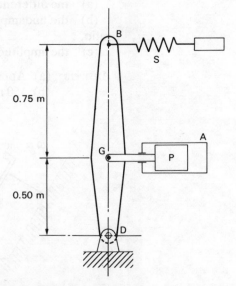

Figure 3.48 Diagram for Problem 3.9.

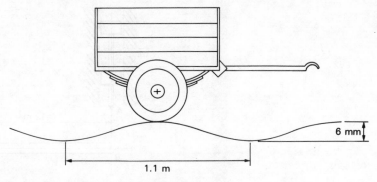

Figure 3.49 Diagram for Problem 3.10.

3.10 A trailer of mass 500 kg forms a spring–mass–damper system, with a single degree of freedom, as shown in Figure 3.49. The equivalent stiffness of the trailer's springs and tyres is 5.25 MN/m and the damping constant is 20 kN/(m/s).

The trailer is pulled over a road surface that can be regarded as a sine wave with an amplitude of 6 mm and a wavelength of 1.1 m. The wheels always remain in contact with the road.

If the speed of the trailer is 17 m/s, what will be the amplitude of the vertical displacement of the trailer?

Answer 16.7 mm.

3.11 A light shaft has a stiffness in torsion of 100 N m/rad. The shaft is fixed at one end and free at the other. Halfway along the length of the shaft is a rotor of moment of inertia of 0.24 kg m². Given that the free end of the shaft is given a torsional oscillation which has an angular displacement of amplitude 1° and a frequency of 3 Hz, find the amplitude of the angular displacement for steady-state torsional oscillation of the rotor.

Answer 0.64°.

3.12 An instrument of mass 15 kg rests on four spring supports each of stiffness 250 N/m. A dashpot is also provided between the instrument and the floor, and it has a resistance of 45 N at 1 m/s velocity. The floor has a vertical sinusoidal motion of amplitude 1 mm and frequency 1.26 Hz.

Determine the amplitude of the displacement for the steady-state motion of the instrument for the above conditions.

Answer 2.94 mm.

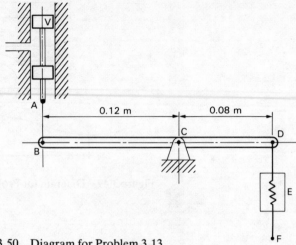

Figure 3.50   Diagram for Problem 3.13.

3.13   Figure 3.50 shows a mechanism, lying in the horizontal plane, used to operate a hydraulic spool valve V. The link BCD is connected at B to the spool valve by means of the link AB, and at D to the input signal point F by means of the spring box E. The spool valve has a mass of 4 kg and viscous forces at the valve are equivalent to a damping coefficient of 10 N s/m. The spring at E has a stiffness of 1.6 kN/m and the moment of inertia of BCD about the fixed axis at C is 0.072 kg m².

The point F is subjected to a harmonic displacement of amplitude 2 mm at a frequency of 1 Hz. For the subsequent steady-state forced vibration of the system where the angular displacement of the lever BCD can be assumed to be small, determine:

(a)   the amplitude of the motion of the spool valve, and
(b)   the amplitude of the force in the link AB.

Answers   (a) 5.9 mm (b) 1.0 N.

3.14   A machine is mounted, as shown in Figure 3.51, on a rigid beam which is pivoted at one end and supported at the other end by

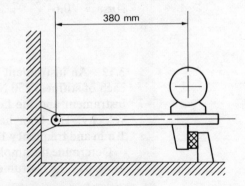

Figure 3.51   Diagram for Problem 3.14.

a rubber block. From a free vibration test the natural damped frequency of the system is found to be 14.982 Hz and the logarithmic decrement 0.314.

The beam and motor have a combined mass of 4.5 kg, a centre of mass at 200 mm from the pivot, and a radius of gyration about the pivot of 300 mm.

Given that the motor is running at 900 rev/min and producing a vertical out-of-balance simple harmonic force of this frequency, find the ratio of the amplitude of the force at the pivot to the amplitude of the out-of-balance force.

Neglect friction at the pivot and assume small displacements throughout.

Answer 1.56.

3.15 Two uniform rods AB and BC are welded together at right angles at B, as shown in Figure 3.52. AB has a mass of 3.0 kg and length of 400 mm, whilst BC has a mass of 1.5 kg and length of 200 mm. The welded rods are pivoted about a fixed point at B. At A a spring of stiffness 20 kN/m is attached and at C a viscous damper provides a damping force of 350 N at 1 m/s. The piston D of the damper has a mass of 2 kg.

In the static equilibrium position AB and CE are parallel with the surface XX. The system shown in Figure 3.52 is in the horizontal plane.

At A a harmonic force of amplitude 50 N and frequency 10 Hz is applied perpendicular to XX. Determine the following:
(a) the moment of inertia of the welded rod about rotation axis through B,

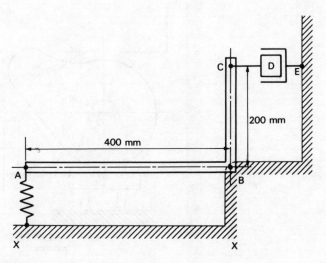

Figure 3.52 Diagram for Problem 3.15.

(b) the differential equation describing small angular oscillations of the welded rod about the equilibrium position,
(c) the undamped natural frequency and the damping ratio,
(d) the amplitude of the displacement of the rods at A,
(e) the amplitude of the force in the rod CD.

Answers (a) 0.18 kg m²
  (b) $\ddot{\theta} + 53.846\dot{\theta} + 12307.7\theta = 76.923 \sin 62.83t$
  (c) 17.66 Hz, 0.2427 (d) 3.41 mm (e) 39.86 N.

3.16 See Figure 3.53. The axle A of an eccentric is mounted in a frame which is supported by anti-vibration mounts which combine the characteristics of an elastic spring and a viscous damper. When the eccentric rotates at constant speed about its axis, it causes steady-state vertical vibrations of the assembly on its mounts.
The following experimental data are available:
(a) free, damped vertical vibrations give a logarithmic decrement of 0.6;
(b) the mounts compress by 23 mm due to the weight of the assembly; and
(c) an oscilloscope display shows a signal whose amplitude is proportional to the force exerted by the mounts on the foundation during steady-state conditions; the display also shows a reference 'blip' which is triggered by a pin on the eccentric once per revolution; when the eccentric angular speed is 15 rad/s the angle ε is 32°.
(i) Working from the equation for the vertical motion of the assembly, derive an expression for the amplitude of the steady-state vertical vibrations of the frame as a function of the amplitude F_t of the transmitted force, the angular speed ω of the rotating eccentric and of the vibrating mass m of the assembly. Sketch the corresponding phasor diagram.

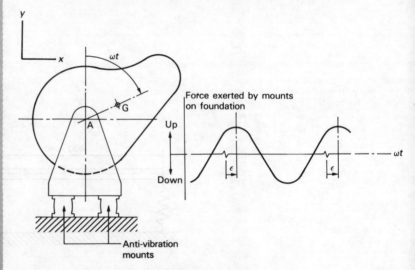

Figure 3.53   Diagram for Problem 3.16.

(ii) For the case when the eccentric rotates with an angular velocity of 15 rad/s, show on a diagram the angular position of the trigger pin causing the blip, relative to the line AG (see Figure 3.53).

Answers (i) $(F_t/m)\{426.52^2 + (3.926\omega)^2\}^{-0.5}$ (ii) 40.4°.

3.17 Figure 3.54 shows the elements of a seismometer, used for measuring movements of the earth's surface. The beam AB, of negligible mass and 100 mm long, pivots freely at B and carries a lumped mass of 1 kg at A. A light spring of free length 100 mm and stiffness 30 N/m is attached between A and C. The compressed length AC is controlled by a screw adjuster. Torsional stiffness and viscous damping act on AB at B in addition. When the seismometer is in equilibrium on a horizontal surface, AB is horizontal and C is in line with AB. With the spring AC removed, the natural undamped frequency of the mass and beam is found to be 1 Hz, and the damping ratio 0.3.

Obtain the linearized equation of motion for small angular displacements of the beam when the horizontal surface has a vertical sinusoidal motion $y = y_0 \sin \omega t$, and the spring AC is compressed to a length of 65 mm. Obtain an expression for the variation of the amplitude θ_0 of the angular displacement θ of AB as a function of ω, and find the new undamped natural frequency.

Answers Linearized equation is $\ddot{\theta} + 3.77\dot{\theta} + 12.825\theta = -10\ddot{y}$,
$$\theta_0/y_0 = 10\omega^2/\{(12.825 - \omega^2)^2 + (3.77\omega)^2\}^{0.5}, 0.57 \text{ Hz}.$$

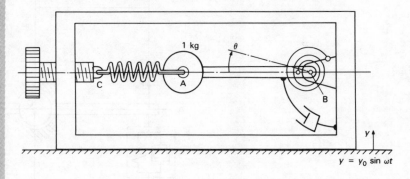

Figure 3.54   Diagram for Problem 3.17.

3.18 A four-cylinder in-line reciprocating engine is fixed to a bedplate which is mounted on vibration isolators. The vibration isolators have a combined stiffness of 2.2 MN/m. The cranks of the engine are disposed so that cranks for cylinders 1 and 2 are at 180° to each other, cranks for cylinders 2 and 3 are at 0° to each other, and cranks 3 and 4 are at 180°. The reciprocating parts in each cylinder have a mass of 1.25 kg and the total mass of the engine is 170 kg. The crank radius is 55 mm and the connecting rod length between centres is 240 mm.

Assume the engine to form a system with a single degree of freedom, in which the engine block executes vertical vibrations.

Determine the amplitude of displacement for steady-state vibrations when the engine is running at 1300 rev/min.

(*Note* This question requires some knowledge of the balancing of reciprocating engines. In the engine described here the primary forces balance, but the secondary forces give rise to a harmonic excitation force whose amplitude depends upon the connecting rod length. The frequency of the resultant secondary force is twice the engine speed.)

Answer 0.11 mm.

3.19 Figure 3.55 shows the torque arm of a torsional test rig which can rotate about O. A shaker S_1, with a mounting of effective stiffness K and damping constant c, applies a force $\mathbf{F_A} = +F_0 \sin(\omega t)\mathbf{j}$ at a point A at one end of the torque arm, while at the same time an identical shaker S_2 applies a force $\mathbf{F_B} = -F_0 \sin(\omega t - \psi)\mathbf{j}$ at the point B at the other end of the torque arm.

The centre of mass of the arm and attached shaker masses is at O, and the total moment of inertia about O is I. Given that the

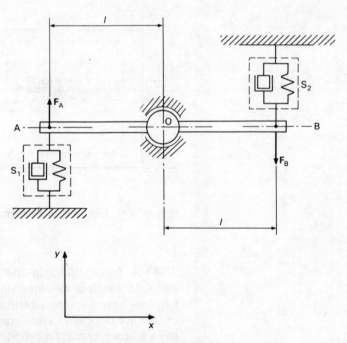

Figure 3.55 Diagram for Problem 3.19.

amplitude of the small angle through which the arm oscillates is X, show that:

$$F_0 = \frac{IX[\{(2Kl^2/I) - \omega^2\}^2 + (2cl^2\omega/I)^2]^{0.5}}{2l \cos (\psi/2)}.$$

Hence show that the reaction on the torque arm through O is:

$$-2(IX/2l) \cos (\omega t - \psi/2) \tan (\psi/2)[(2Kl^2/I - \omega^2)^2 + (2cl^2\omega/I)^2]^{0.5}.$$

4

Energy methods

The basic differential equation of harmonic motion, and hence the natural frequency, may be obtained by using the energy equation as well as directly from Newton's second law by using free-body diagrams. We consider here the motion of a conservative system. The word 'conservative' here means that all energy of the system is conserved. The energy equation for a conservative system is:

$$\Delta T + \Delta V_g + \Delta V_e = 0, \qquad [4.1]$$

where T is the kinetic energy,
V_g is the gravitational potential energy,
V_e is the elastic potential energy.

The Δ in this equation means change (or difference), thus ΔT is the change in kinetic energy of the system or the difference between the kinetic energy at some final state of the system (or state 2) and the kinetic energy at some initial state (state 1). What happens between the initial and the final states does not concern us here. For a conservative system the total energy of the system at the final state is equal to the total energy at the initial state of the system. This energy, of course, is constant. So

$$T_1 + V_{g1} + V_{e1} = T_2 + V_{g2} + V_{e2} \qquad [4.2]$$
$$= \text{constant}.$$

4.1 Kinetic energy

For plane motion the kinetic energy of a rigid body of mass m is given by:

$$T = 0.5mv_G^2 + 0.5I_G\omega^2,$$

where I_G is the moment of inertia of the body about an axis through the mass centre G of the body. This axis is perpendicular to the plane of the motion. v_G is the velocity of mass centre G (in vector notation $\mathbf{v}_G = \dot{x}_G\mathbf{i} + \dot{y}_G\mathbf{j}$). ω (or $\dot{\theta}$) is the angular velocity of the rigid body. If the body has translation alone, then $\omega = 0$ and $T = 0.5mv_G^2$. For a rigid body which is rolling about an axis through the instantaneous centre C, as in Figure 1.6(a), the body's total kinetic energy is given by $T = 0.5I_C\omega^2$, where I_C is the moment of inertia of the body about an axis through C. Similarly, a rigid body which has only rotation about a fixed axis through O has kinetic energy $0.5I_O\omega^2$, where I_O is the moment of inertia of the body about the fixed axis of rotation.

4.2 Potential energy

Gravitational potential energy (potential energy of position) of a body of
mass m in a gravitational field is given by:

$$V_g = mgh,$$

where h is the height of the centre of mass of the body above an arbitrary
datum position (reference position).

Elastic potential energy of a spring (strain energy) is given by:

$$V_e = 0.5ky_0^2,$$

where k is the stiffness of the spring or spring constant and y_0 is the
extension or compression of the spring (change of the spring length).

4.3 Application of energy method to spring–mass system of Figure 1.1(a)

Figure 4.1(a) shows the rigid body of mass m in static equilibrium with the
spring extended by y_0. We choose the static equilibrium position as the
datum position for the gravitational potential energy. In static equilibrium
the total energy of the system is only that of elastic potential energy and is
equal to $0.5ky_0^2$. If the body is now displaced downwards by y from the
equilibrium position (Figure 4.1(b)) the total energy of the system at this
final state is given by:

$$0.5m\dot{y}^2 \quad - \quad mgy \quad + \quad 0.5k(y_0 + y)^2.$$
$$\text{(K.E.)} \quad \text{(gravitational P.E.)} \quad \text{(elastic P.E.)}$$

The gravitational potential energy is negative because the body is now
below the datum position. For a conservative system the total energies of
the system corresponding to both states (Figures 4.1(a) and 4.1(b)) must
be equal, so

$$0.5ky_0^2 = 0.5m\dot{y}^2 - mgy + 0.5k(y_0 + y)^2 \qquad [4.3]$$
$$= \text{constant.}$$

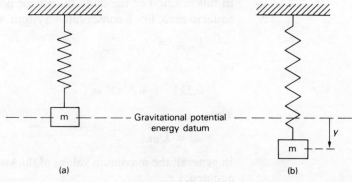

Figure 4.1 (a) Body in equilibrium, (b) Body displaced from equilibrium
position.

Hence

$$0.5ky_0^2 = 0.5m\dot{y}^2 - mgy + 0.5ky_0^2 + kyy_0 + 0.5ky^2$$

or

$$0 = 0.5m\dot{y}^2 - mgy + kyy_0 + 0.5ky^2.$$

But $mg = ky_0$, and hence

$$0 = 0.5m\dot{y}^2 + 0.5ky^2. \hspace{2cm} [4.4]$$

Differentiation of equation [4.4] with respect to time gives a power equation:

$$0 = m\dot{y}\ddot{y} + ky\dot{y}.$$

Therefore either $\dot{y} = 0$ (which occurs at the maximum or minimum displacement of the system from static equilibrium position) or:

$$\ddot{y} + (k/m)y = 0.$$

The above equation is the same as equation [1.2].

Normally equation [4.4] is used instead of equation [4.3]. In equation [4.4] we have neither such energy terms as $0.5ky_0$ nor gravitational energy terms. If the datum position for gravitational energy is taken as the static equilibrium position, then the mean gravitational potential energy over a cycle of the vibration is zero. This is not the case with the kinetic or elastic potential energies because squared terms are involved in the averaging over a cycle.

The natural frequency of the system vibration can be obtained directly from the energy equation. For example, let us consider the undamped system such as shown in Figure 4.1. We can assume that the displacement of the body during vibration is described by $y = Y \cos \omega_n t$. Then the maximum value of the elastic potential energy of the system, $V_{e,max}$, is $0.5kY^2$, and is reached by the system at the lowest and highest positions of the body during the oscillation. It should be noted that at these positions of the body the kinetic energy of the system is equal to zero. Similarly, the system has the maximum kinetic energy, T_{max}, when the body passes through the equilibrium position and then $T_{max} = 0.5mY^2\omega_n^2$. In this position of the body the elastic potential energy of the system is equal to zero. For a conservative system, we may write:

$$V_{e,max} = T_{max}$$

or

$$0.5kY^2 = 0.5mY^2\omega_n^2.$$

Thus

$$\omega_n^2 = k/m.$$

In general, the maximum values of the kinetic and potential energies are equated, i.e.,

$$V_{max} = T_{max}. \hspace{2cm} [4.5]$$

We should note that equation [4.4] refers to the kinetic energy and potential energy at a particular instant of time, whereas equation [4.5] is equating maximum potential and kinetic energies of the system at different instants of time during the oscillation.

**Example 4.1
Determination of
natural frequency
using energy method**

Obtain the natural frequency of vibration of the system shown in Example 1.5 (and Figure 1.9) using the energy method.

Solution   We will consider the spring–mass displacement relative to the static equilibrium position of this system, i.e., we will disregard the gravitational potential energy and those energy components which have constant values during vibration (see the energy equation [4.3]). Figure 1.11(b) will be useful in this discussion. If the pulley rotates through an angle θ about an axis through its instantaneous centre C and if y is the displacement of the pulley's geometric centre, then $2y$ is the extension of the spring.

The energy terms, which sum to zero, are shown below:

$$0.5\,I_G\omega^2 \quad + \quad 0.5mv_G^2 \quad + \quad 0.5Mv_G^2 \quad + \quad 0.5k(2y)^2 \;=0.$$
(pulley K.E.-   (pulley K.E.-   (load K.E.-   (spring
rotational)   translational)   translational)   elastic P.E.)

As $y = 0.6\theta$, $\dot{y} = 0.6\dot{\theta}$. But $\dot{y}$ denotes v_G and $\dot{\theta}$ denotes ω, hence:

$$0.5 \times 20 \times 0.3^2\dot{\theta}^2 + 0.5 \times 20(0.6\dot{\theta})^2 + 0.5 \times 25(0.6\dot{\theta})^2$$
$$+ \; 0.5 \times 500(2 \times 0.6\theta)^2 = 0$$

or

$$0.5(1.8 + 7.2 + 9.0)\dot{\theta}^2 + 0.5(720)\theta^2 = 0,$$
$$0.5 \times 18\dot{\theta}^2 + 0.5 \times 720\theta^2 = 0.$$

Differentiating the above equation with respect to time leads to

$$18\ddot{\theta} + 720\theta = 0$$

or

$$\ddot{\theta} + 40\theta = 0.$$

Previously (see Example 1.5) we had a differential equation in terms of y, not θ, but, as y and θ are related to each other by a constant, the equations are interchangeable. Thus

$$\omega_n = 40^{0.5} \quad \text{and} \quad f_n = 1.01\,\text{Hz}.$$

Answer   Natural frequency is **1.01 Hz.**

Example 4.2
Analysis of a system
with beam and drum
by energy method

Figure 4.2 shows diagrammatically the arrangement of a temporary hoist. The rigid uniform beam AC has a mass of 30 kg, carries the hoisting drum at C, and is pinned to a fixed support at A. The hoisting cable passes over the drum, which has a centroidal moment of inertia of 1.2 kg m^2 and a mass of 10 kg, to the motor shaft at D. The beam support at B is equivalent to a spring of stiffness 200 kN/m.

Determine, using an energy method or otherwise, the natural frequency of small oscillations of the system about the equilibrium position in which the beam AC is horizontal for the condition when a load of 500 kg is suspended with the hoist motor D braked. Assume that slipping does not occur between the hoist drum and the cable.

When the system is vibrating at this frequency the maximum magnitude of the acceleration of the load is observed to be 0.25 m/s^2. Determine the maximum force in the beam support under these conditions.

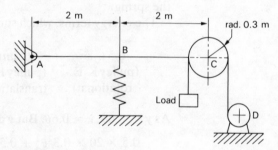

Figure 4.2   Diagram of hoist (Example 4.2).

Solution   If in the above text an energy method is recommended then it is sensible to take this advice.

Method (a). First of all we consider the total energy of the system in the equilibrium position. In this position the system (hoist) will have some energy arising from the compressed spring as well as the gravitational potential energy of the system.

If y_0 is the initial compression of the spring, then the elastic potential energy stored in the spring is $0.5ky_0^2$, where k is the stiffness of the spring (200 kN/m). For the gravitational potential energy we require a datum position. If we take the static equilibrium position as the reference, then the gravitational potential energy of the system at this position is zero. Thus the initial total energy is given by a term which has the constant value:

$$0.5ky_0^2 = \text{constant.}$$

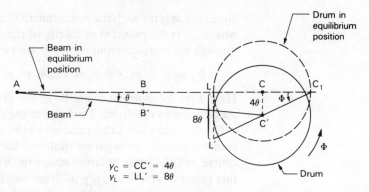

$$y_C = CC' = 4\theta$$
$$y_L = LL' = 8\theta$$

Figure 4.3   Diagram (not to scale) showing displacement of beam and drum (Example 4.2).

As the hoist can be regarded as a conservative system, the total energy of this system remains constant, although an expression for the total energy of the system will be made up of different terms that vary as the free vibration takes place.

Let us now analyse the different energy terms of the total energy of the hoist system (beam with support, hoisting drum, load), when the system is not in its equilibrium position. Let the beam be deflected clockwise through an angle θ (Figure 4.3) during the vibration. Figures 4.2 and 4.3 show that the spring is compressed by an amount 2θ in addition to the initial compression of y_0. The elastic potential energy stored in the spring is now $0.5k(y_0 + 2\theta)^2$.

As the beam rotates clockwise it loses gravitational potential energy relative to the datum position of amount $30g \times 2\theta$ and the centre of mass of the drum moves downwards and the drum loses gravitational potential energy of the amount $10g \times 4\theta$. Next let us consider the potential energy of the load. As the beam rotates clockwise the drum (mass centre C) turns anti-clockwise and the load descends. To find out how much the load descends we have to realize that the point C_1 (Figure 4.3) is an instantaneous centre of rotation. So long as the beam has small deflections from its equilibrium (horizontal) position the drum displacement is as shown in Figure 4.3. The displacement of C, the centre of the drum, is 4θ because the drum is attached to the beam of length 4 m. The displacement of the point L is 8θ, and this is the amount by which the load descends. The gravitational potential energy of the load in relation to its reference position is thus $-500g \times 8\theta$. The negative sign is required because the load has lost potential energy relative to the datum position.

Analysing next the kinetic energy of the whole system, we find that the beam rotates about a fixed axis through A and therefore has kinetic energy of $0.5I_A\dot{\theta}^2$, where $I_A = 30 \times 4^2/3 \text{ kg m}^2$. I_A is the moment of inertia of the beam about the rotation axis through A. Thus the beam kinetic energy is $0.5 \times 160\dot{\theta}^2$.

The drum motion can be considered as purely rotational. The drum has an angular velocity of $\dot{\Phi}$ (see Figure 4.3) and its kinetic energy of rotation about the axis through the instantaneous centre of rotation C_1 is $0.5I_{C1}\dot{\Phi}^2$, where I_{C1} is the moment of inertia of the drum about the rotational axis through the instantaneous centre C_1 and where

$$I_{C1} = I_C + m \times 0.3^2 = 1.2 + 10 \times 0.09 = 2.1 \text{ kg m}^2.$$

Here I_C is the moment of inertia of the drum about the axis through the mass centre of the drum. The mass of the drum is m.

On the other hand this rotation of the drum can be considered as the composition of two separate motions: the translation of the drum mass centre and the drum rotation about the axis through its mass centre. In this case the kinetic energy of drum rotation is $0.5I_C\dot{\Phi}^2$ and the kinetic energy of translation for the drum is $0.5mv_C^2$, where v_C is the velocity of C, the centre of mass of the drum. Thus the kinetic energy of translation for the drum is $0.5 \times 10(4\dot{\theta})^2$.

The relation between θ and Φ follows from Figure 4.3 and is:

$$0.3\Phi = 4\theta$$

and

$$\dot{\Phi} = 4\dot{\theta}/0.3.$$

Thus the total kinetic energy of the drum

$$
\begin{aligned}
&= 0.5I_C\dot{\Phi}^2 + 0.5mv_C^2 \\
&= 0.5(I_C + m \times 0.3^2)\dot{\Phi}^2 \\
&= 0.5I_{C1}\dot{\Phi}^2 \quad \text{(by using the parallel-axes theorem).}
\end{aligned}
$$

This is the same result as for the case of drum rotation about the instantaneous centre C_1.

Finally, as the displacement of the load is 8θ, the kinetic energy of the load is $0.5 \times 500(8\dot{\theta})^2$.

We now add all the energy terms and equate them to the total energy of the whole system in the initial (equilibrium) position:

$$0.5k(y_0 + 2\theta)^2 - 30g \times 2\theta - 10g \times 4\theta - 500g \times 8\theta$$

(spring elastic   (beam grav.   (drum grav.   (load grav.
P.E.)   P.E.)   P.E.)   P.E.)

$$+ 0.5 \times 160\dot{\theta}^2 + 0.5 \times 1.2(4\dot{\theta}/0.3)^2 + 0.5 \times 10(4\dot{\theta})^2$$

(beam rotat.   (drum rotational   (drum transl.
K.E.)   K.E.)   K.E.)

$$+ 0.5 \times 500(8\dot{\theta})^2 = \quad 0.5ky_0^2.$$

(load K.E.)   (initial P.E.-
spring elastic
energy)

Hence

$$0.5ky_0^2 + 2ky_0\theta + 2k\theta^2 - 4100g\theta + 16266.7\dot{\theta}^2 = 0.5ky_0^2.$$

Clearly, the $0.5ky_0^2$ terms on either side cancel out, but we are still left with the term $2ky_0\theta$. We are able to obtain an expression for this term by considering the equilibrium position of the system and analysing moments about the axis through point A. The result is:

$$2ky_0 = 2 \times 30g + 4 \times 10g + 4 \times 2 \times 500g.$$

Let us note that the situation when the 500 kg load is suspended at the point L of the drum is equivalent to locating a 1000 kg load at C. (Draw a free-body diagram of the drum to confirm this point.) Thus

$$2ky_0\theta = 4100g\theta.$$

Hence the final energy equation is:

$$2k\theta^2 + 16\,266.7\dot\theta^2 = 0.$$

Let us differentiate the above equation with respect to time:

$$4k\dot\theta\theta + 2 \times 16\,266.7\ddot\theta\dot\theta = 0.$$

Therefore,

$$\ddot\theta + (2k/16\,266.7)\theta = 0.$$

This is the differential equation for simple harmonic motion of the system and the undamped circular natural frequency of vibration is given by:

$$\omega_n^2 = 2 \times 200\,000/16\,266.7.$$
$$\omega_n = 4.96 \text{ rad/s} \quad \text{and} \quad f_n = 0.789 \text{ Hz.}$$

Answer Natural frequency is **0.789 Hz.**

Method (b). The above, lengthy discussion takes into account all the energy terms. If we realize that the gravitational potential energy terms cancel out with part of the elastic potential energy, then the only elastic energy term that remains is a function of θ alone and the following energy equation is obtained:

$$\underset{\substack{\text{(spring}\\ \text{elastic P.E.)}}}{0.5k(2\theta)^2} + \underset{\text{(beam K.E.)}}{0.5 \times 160\dot\theta^2} + \underset{\text{(drum K.E.)}}{0.5 \times 2.1(4\dot\theta/0.3)^2}$$
$$+ \underset{\text{(load K.E.)}}{0.5 \times 500(8\dot\theta)^2} = 0.$$

This leads to the same final differential equation as before. It should be noted that the kinetic energy of the drum has been reduced to pure rotational kinetic energy by recognizing that C_1 is the instantaneous centre of rotation. Therefore the kinetic energy of the drum is $0.5I_{C1}\dot\Phi^2$. Using the parallel-axes theorem we obtain

$$I_{C1} = 1.2 + 10 \times 0.3^2 \text{ kg m}^2,$$

as mentioned previously.

Next we have to obtain the maximum force in the beam support when the maximum magnitude of the acceleration of the load is 0.25 m/s². Displacement y_B of B is 2θ and the displacement y_L of the load is 8θ. Hence when the maximum magnitude of the load acceleration is 0.25 m/s², we have:

$$|8\ddot{\theta}|_{max} = 0.25.$$

But $|\ddot{\theta}|_{max} = \theta_0 \omega_n^2$, where θ_0 is the amplitude of angular displacement θ. Hence

$$\theta_0 = 0.25/(8 \times 4.96^2)$$

and

$$y_{B,max} = 2 \times 0.25/(8 \times 4.96^2) = 2.54 \times 10^{-3} \, \text{m}.$$

Thus the amplitude of the force in the support is $ky_{B,max}$, where

$$ky_{B,max} = 200 \times 10^3 \times 2.54 \times 10^{-3} = 508 \, \text{N}.$$

The force in the support at static equilibrium is 20 111 N, hence the maximum force in the support is **20 619 N**.

Example 4.3
Measurement of moment of inertia by rolling oscillation

The moment of inertia of the rotor of a small fan is to be measured using the method of rolling oscillations. In this method a pendulum, which in this case takes the form of a slender, uniform rectangular bar, is attached to the shaft of the rotor, so that the rotor is able to oscillate whilst the shaft is rolling on the straight, parallel rails, as shown in Figure 4.4. The rotor has been previously balanced so that its mass centre O lies on the axis of rotation. The rotor and pendulum are set into small amplitude oscillations and the time period is measured.

Show that the undamped circular natural frequency ω_n is given by:

$$\omega_n^2 = mgh/[(Mr^2 + I_O) + m\{(h - r)^2 + k_{G1}^2\}],$$

where m = mass of pendulum,
M = mass of rotor and axle,
r = radius of rotor axle,
h = distance from the axis of rotation of the rotor to the mass centre of the pendulum,
k_{G1} = radius of gyration of pendulum about an axis through the pendulum mass centre at G1,
I_O = moment of inertia of rotor (and axle) about an axis through O (see Figure 4.5).

For the values characterizing the system, shown in Figure 4.5, estimate a value for I_O if 40 oscillations take 24.1 s.

Solution Let us assume that at a certain instant in time the pendulum is inclined at an angle θ to the vertical position. The rotor on its axle rolls on the rails, hence

$$v_O = r\dot{\theta} \quad \text{and} \quad v_{G1} = (h - r)\dot{\theta} = h\dot{\theta} - v_O,$$

where v_O is the velocity of the centre of mass of the rotor and v_{G1} is the velocity of the mass centre of the pendulum, G1.

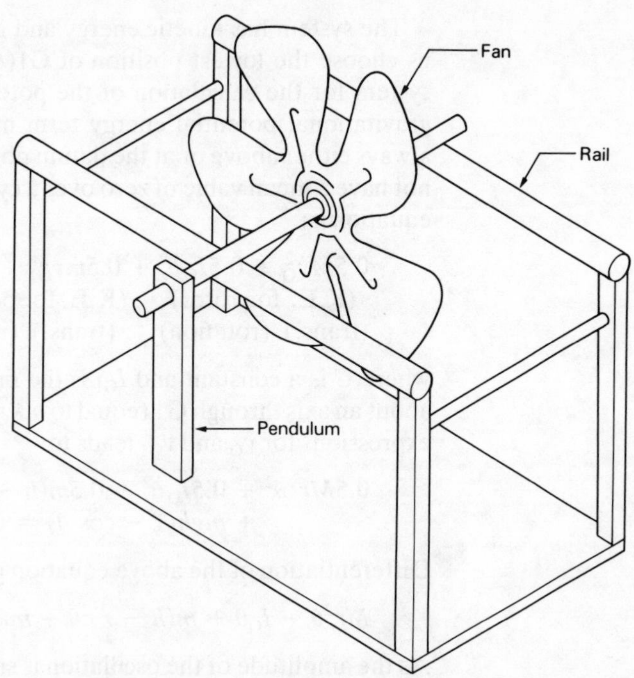

Figure 4.4 Apparatus for determining moment of inertia by rolling oscillation (Example 4.3).

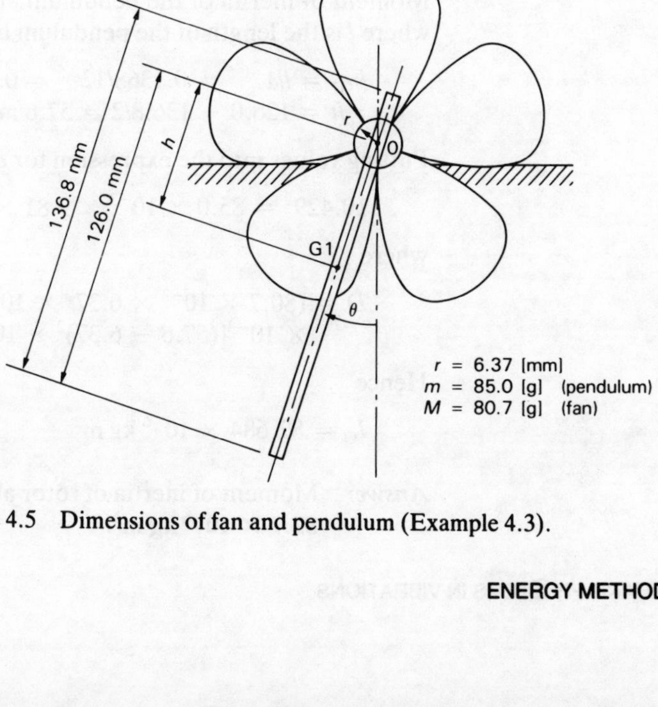

Figure 4.5 Dimensions of fan and pendulum (Example 4.3).

The system has kinetic energy and gravitational potential energy. Let us choose the lowest position of G1($\theta = 0$) as a datum position of the system for the calculation of the potential energy. In this example the gravitational potential energy term must be considered because G1 is always either above or at the datum position and therefore this term does not have a mean value of zero over a cycle of vibration. Hence the energy equation is:

$$0.5Mv_O^2 + 0.5I_O\dot{\theta}^2 + 0.5mv_{G1}^2 + 0.5I_{G1}\dot{\theta}^2 + mgh(1 - \cos\theta) = C,$$

(K.E. for rotor)   (K.E. for pendulum)   (P.E. for pendulum)
(trans.) (rotation)   (trans.) (rotation)

where C is a constant and I_{G1} is the moment of inertia of the pendulum about an axis through G1 (equal to mk_{G1}^2). Substitution of the appropriate expressions for v_O and v_{G1} leads to:

$$0.5Mr^2\dot{\theta}^2 + 0.5I_O\dot{\theta}^2 + 0.5m(h-r)^2\dot{\theta}^2 + 0.5mk_{G1}^2\dot{\theta}^2$$
$$+ mgh(1 - \cos\theta) = C.$$

Differentiation of the above equation gives:

$$Mr^2\ddot{\theta} + I_O\ddot{\theta} + m(h-r)^2\ddot{\theta} + mk_{G1}^2\ddot{\theta} + mgh\sin\theta = 0.$$

As the amplitude of the oscillation is small, $\sin\theta = \theta$, hence

$$\{Mr^2 + I_O + m(h-r)^2 + mk_{G1}^2\}\ddot{\theta} + mgh\theta = 0.$$

Hence

$$\omega_n^2 = mgh/[(Mr^2 + I_O) + m\{(h-r)^2 + k_{G1}^2\}].$$

Solution of the numerical part of the question: the time period of the oscillations is 24.1/40 = 0.6025 s. Hence

$$\omega_n = 2\pi/0.6025 = 10.429 \text{ rad/s.}$$

Moment of inertia of the pendulum about an axis through G1 is $ml^2/12$, where l is the length of the pendulum bar, and hence

$$k_{G1} = l/12^{0.5} = 0.1368/12^{0.5} = 0.03949 \text{ m} \quad (39.49 \text{ mm}).$$
$$h = 126.0 - 136.8/2 = 57.6 \text{ mm.}$$

Putting values into the expression for ω_n^2 we obtain

$$10.429^2 = 85.0 \times 10^{-3} \times 9.81 \times 57.6 \times 10^{-3}/D,$$

where

$$D = (80.7 \times 10^{-3} \times 6.37^2 \times 10^{-6} + I_O) + 85.0$$
$$\times 10^{-3}[(57.6 - 6.37)^2 \times 10^{-6} + 39.49^2 \times 10^{-6}].$$

Hence

$$I_O = 82.684 \times 10^{-6} \text{ kg m}^2.$$

Answer   Moment of inertia of rotor about its axis (I_O) is
82.7×10^{-6} kg m^2.

Example 4.4
Energy method
applied to a simple
mechanism

Figure 4.6 shows a mechanism in which the sliders A and B move along fixed perpendicular guides, connected by the uniform, slender link AB of mass 4 kg. The slider A is under the action of a spring of stiffness 3 kN/m. In the equilibrium position BC is 0.3 m.

Determine the natural frequency of small oscillations of the system.

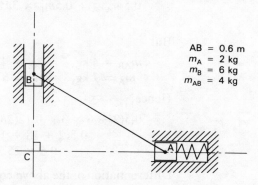

AB = 0.6 m
m_A = 2 kg
m_B = 6 kg
m_{AB} = 4 kg

Figure 4.6   Diagram for Example 4.4.

Solution   If BC is 0.3 m then in the equilibrium position angle CAB is 30° (see Figure 4.7). If we are to use the energy method we need information on the velocities of the sliders as well as the link AB. This is most easily obtained by constructing a velocity diagram for the mechanism, as shown in Figure 4.7. It is convenient to express all magnitudes of the velocities in terms of v_A, the magnitude of the velocity of the slider A. Thus:

$$v_B = 3^{0.5}v_A,$$

the magnitude of the velocity of the centre of the link AB (v_G) = v_A, the magnitude of the angular velocity of the link AB (ω_{AB}) = $(2/0.6)v_A$.

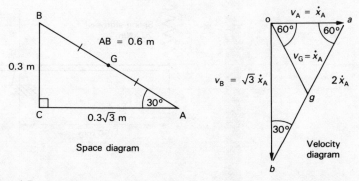

Figure 4.7   Space and velocity diagrams for mechanism shown in Figure 4.6.

When the slider A is displaced by x_A the energy equation for the system as a whole is:

$$\underbrace{0.5m_A v_A^2}_{\text{(K.E. of A)}} + \underbrace{0.5m_B v_B^2}_{\text{(K.E. of B)}} + \underbrace{0.5I_{AB}\omega_{AB}^2}_{\substack{\text{(K.E. of AB}\\\text{-rotation)}}} + \underbrace{0.5m_{AB}v_G^2}_{\substack{\text{(K.E. of AB}\\\text{-translation)}}}$$

$$+ \underbrace{0.5kx_A^2}_{\text{(elastic P.E.)}} = 0$$

or

$$0.5m_A v_A^2 + 0.5m_B \times 3v_A^2 + 0.5I_{AB}(2/0.6)^2 v_A^2$$
$$+ 0.5m_{AB}v_A^2 + 0.5kx_A^2 = 0.$$

But

$$m_{AB} = 4\,\text{kg}, \quad I_{AB} = 4 \times 0.6^2/12 = 0.12\,\text{kg m}^2; \quad I_{AB} \equiv I_G.$$
$$m_A = 2\,\text{kg}, \quad m_B = 6\,\text{kg}.$$

Hence,

$$0.5(2 + 6 \times 3 + 0.12(2/0.6)^2 + 4)v_A^2 + 0.5kx_A^2 = 0$$
$$0.5(2 + 18 + 1.333 + 4)v_A^2 + 0.5kx_A^2 = 0.$$
$$0.5 \times 25.333v_A^2 + 0.5 \times 3000x_A^2 = 0.$$

Differentiation of the above equation gives:

$$25.333\ddot{x}_A + 3000x_A = 0 \quad (v_A = \dot{x}_A).$$

Hence

$$\omega_n^2 = 118.42, \quad \omega_n = 10.88\,\text{rad/s} \quad \text{and} \quad f_n = 1.73\,\text{Hz}.$$

Answer Natural frequency is **1.73 Hz.**

Problems

4.1 A uniform, slender beam of mass 2 kg is pivoted at O and supported horizontally in the equilibrium position by two springs mounted at the ends of the beam, as shown in Figure 4.8. The beam dimensions and spring stiffness values are given in the figure.

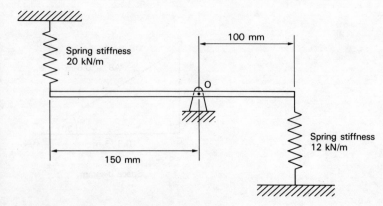

Figure 4.8 Diagram for Problem 4.1.

Use an energy method to obtain the natural frequency of small oscillations of the beam.

Answer 35.18 Hz.

4.2 A solid sphere of radius r rolls without slipping in a hemispherical bowl of radius R.

Use an energy method to find the periodic time of small oscillations of the sphere about its equilibrium position.

Answer $2\pi\{7(R - r)/(5g)\}^{0.5}$.

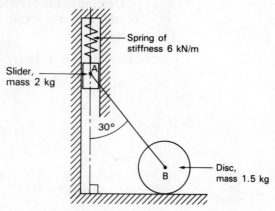

Figure 4.9 Diagram for Problem 4.3.

4.3 Figure 4.9 shows a slider A of mass 2 kg attached by means of a light, rigid link AB to a uniform disc which is pinned to the link at B. The disc has a mass of 1.5 kg. The wheel rolls on a plane which is at a right angle to the direction of motion of the slider. The slider A is attached to a spring of stiffness 6 kN/m, as shown in the figure. In the equilibrium position AB is inclined at an angle of 30° to the direction of motion of slider A.

Estimate the natural frequency of small oscillations of the system.

Answer 4.17 Hz.

4.4 The double arm lever AOB consists of a thin, uniform rod of mass m. The rod is pivoted at the point O. A spring of stiffness k and small body of mass M are attached to the ends of the rod, as shown in Figure 4.10.

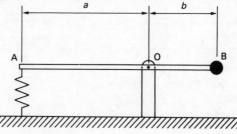

Figure 4.10 Diagram for Problem 4.4.

Using an energy method, determine the natural circular frequency of small oscillations of the system.

Answer $a[k/\{Mb^2 + (1/3)m(a^3 + b^3)/(a + b)\}]^{0.5}$.

4.5 The hollow cylinder of mass M has an internal radius of r_1 and external radius r_2, as shown in Figure 4.11. The cylinder rolls without slipping on a cylindrical surface of radius R. Two additional point masses, each of mass m, are attached opposite to each other on the internal surface of the cylinder.

Determine the circular frequency of small-amplitude oscillations of the cylinder about its equilibrium position. Use an energy method.

Answer $[(M + 2m)gr_2/\{0.5M(r_1^2 + 3r_2^2) + 2m(r_1^2 + r_2^2)\}]^{0.5}$.

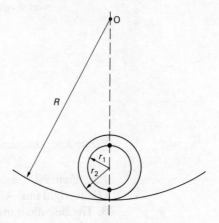

Figure 4.11 Diagram for Problem 4.5.

5

Response of systems with a single degree of freedom to step and other inputs

This chapter deals briefly with methods of solving so-called transient vibration problems.

Let us consider the linear and undamped single degree of freedom system (mass–spring) with an excitation. The excitation of the system can be caused by various factors; it may be a force acting directly on the mass of the system or it may be a ground motion acting on the spring via its anchorage point. The excitation of the system is expressed in terms of a known function of time. In the case of force excitation, the excitation is known in terms of a force function and, in the case of ground motion, it is expressed by means of a displacement function or very often by a ground acceleration function or by a ground velocity.

All differential equations of motion written for each type of excitation may be presented in the simple general form:

$$m\ddot{r} + kr = e(t) \qquad [5.1]$$

or

$$(1/\omega_n^2)\ddot{r} + r = e(t)/k, \qquad [5.2]$$

where $\omega_n^2 = k/m$, and ω_n is the angular (or circular) natural frequency. r and e are the response and the excitation, respectively, at time t.

5.1 Classical method

It was mentioned in Chapter 3 that the complete or general solution of the non-homogeneous linear differential equation is the sum of the particular integral (e.g., for equation [5.1] it is the particular solution of [5.1]) and the complementary function (i.e., in the case of [5.1] the general solution of equation $\ddot{r} + \omega_n^2 r = 0$).

The two constants appearing in the complementary function are determined by the initial conditions. Therefore, to specify a motion of the system we must find a general solution of the differential equation which fulfils the initial conditions for $t = 0$: $r = r_0$, $\dot{r} = \dot{r}_0$; namely:

$$r(t) = \{r_0 - P(0)\} \cos(\omega_n t) + [\{\dot{r}_0 - \dot{P}(0)\}/\omega_n] \sin(\omega_n t) + P(t),$$

where $P(t)$ is a particular solution of [5.1].

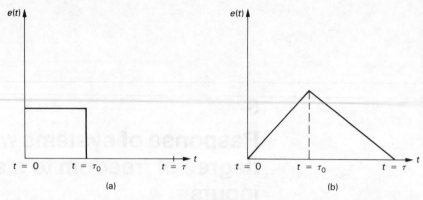

Figure 5.1   (a) Step excitation function; (b) Triangular excitation function.

In general, the form of excitation function and its properties determine the choice of the most appropriate and effective method of solving the differential equation of the system motion. In the classical approach, mentioned above, the problem of finding the solution for the motion of the system, described, e.g., by equation [5.1] and by the appropriate initial conditions, is reduced in practice to determining the particular integral $P(t)$.

Let us assume, e.g., that the excitation functions (force, displacement of the ground, etc.) have the forms shown in Figure 5.1(a) and (b). It will be shown in Example 5.2 that in this case it is not a complicated task to determine the particular solution $P(t)$. The procedure for solving [5.1] for such a form of the excitation function requires a two-stage approach, namely for $0 \leqslant t \leqslant \tau_0$ and $\tau_0 \leqslant t \leqslant \tau$.

5.2   Duhamel's integral method

In Chapter 3, devoted to forced vibrations, we considered a response to periodic excitation (periodic forcing). However, in many problems a dynamical linear system is excited by a suddenly applied aperiodic excitation, e.g., pulse excitation (Figure 5.1). The response to such excitation is called transient and its amplitude varies depending on the type of excitation. However, the system oscillates still with its natural frequency.

The most appropriate method applied to such transient vibration problems in linear systems is the method of Duhamel's integral (called also convolution or superposition integral method). This method is more universal than that previously mentioned as the classical approach, because it can be used in the case of arbitrary non-periodic or discontinuous excitations. However, as was mentioned, for sufficiently simple excitation functions (Examples 5.1, 5.2, 5.3), e.g., for excitation function linearly dependent on time, the classical approach is still more effective than Duhamel's method.

It may be shown that the response to the arbitrary excitation $e(t)$, equation [5.1], is represented by the integral (Duhamel's integral):

$$r(t) = \int_0^t e(\tau)g(t - \tau)\,\mathrm{d}\tau, \qquad\qquad [5.3]$$

where τ is the time at which an excitation impulse was applied and where $g(t - \tau)$ is the response to the unit impulse of excitation $\delta(t - \tau)$; the unit impulse is often called the delta function.

In the case when an excitation is the unit impulse of force acting on an undamped single degree of freedom system, which was previously at rest, the response to this unit impulse of force is:

$$g(t - \tau) = [\sin \{\omega_n(t - \tau)\}]/(m\omega_n), \qquad\qquad [5.4]$$

where ω_n is the angular natural frequency of the system.

To develop a proof of equation [5.3], one should analyse [5.4], a response to the unit impulse excitation, and consider the arbitrary impulse to be a sequence of short impulses. Then, when the system is linear the principle of superposition may be employed and by summing all the contributions of the impulses to the response at time t one obtains [5.3]. (See Timoshenko *et al.*, *Vibration Problems in Engineering* (4th edn), Wiley, 1974, for a further discussion of Duhamel's integral.)

5.3   The Laplace method

An alternate method is that of Laplace which is very important in solving linear differential equations.

The Laplace transform $F(s)$ of a known function of t, $f(t)$, where $t > 0$, is defined by the equation:

$$F(s) = \int_0^\infty e^{-st}f(t)\,\mathrm{d}t = \mathcal{L}[f(t)], \qquad\qquad [5.5]$$

where s, in general, is a complex variable. The integral exists if $\lim_{t \to \infty} e^{-st}f(t) = 0$.

To find a solution of a differential equation by Laplace transformation we should first transform the differential equation, in the variable t, into an algebraic equation in the complex variable s. When the algebraic equation obtained is solved, the next step is to determine the solution of the differential equation by an inverse transformation, $f(t) = \mathcal{L}^{-1}[F(s)]$, of the solution of the algebraic equation.

5.4   The Fourier method

Similarly, as with Duhamel's method and the Laplace method, Fourier's approach is particularly useful for an analysis of transient motions.

The Fourier transform of a function $f(t)$ exists if $f(t)$ is absolutely integrable, i.e. if $\int_{-\infty}^{+\infty} |f(t)|\,\mathrm{d}t$ is convergent and if $f(t)$ satisfies the Dirichlet conditions:

(a) $f(t)$ is single valued;
(b) $f(t)$ is piecewise continuous;
(c) $f(t)$ has a finite number of maxima and minima.

The definitions of the Fourier transform (transformation of function $f(t)$) and its inverse, called a Fourier-transform pair, are:

$$F(\omega) = \int_{-\infty}^{+\infty} f(t)\, e^{-i\omega t}\, dt, \qquad [5.6]$$

$$f(t) = \int_{-\infty}^{+\infty} \{F(\omega)\, e^{i\omega t}/(2\pi)\}\, d\omega. \qquad [5.7]$$

The definitions of Laplace and Fourier transforms point out common properties of both. The Laplace transform, which is a one-sided time function, is not much more than a special case of the Fourier transform. However, methods of solving differential equations that are based on the Laplace transform are significantly more general and powerful than Fourier methods.

The procedure for solving differential equations by Fourier transformation is similar to the procedure in Laplace's method. A choice of the most appropriate method depends in general on the properties of differential equations and initial conditions. In the case considered (e.g., equation [5.1]) for the same initial condition methods should be determined by the character of the excitation function.

5.5 The phase-plane method

Finally, the phase-plane method in graphical form is very often applied to solving linear transient vibration problems. This method can be also useful in some non-linear vibrations problems.

A system with a single degree of freedom requires two parameters, namely, velocity and displacement, to describe completely the state of the vibration. When these two parameters are used as co-ordinate axes the motion can be visualized in the so-called phase plane.

The phase plane is a plane of $(\dot{r}/\omega_n, r)$ in the $\dot{r}/\omega_n, r$ co-ordinate system. We shall explain the phase-plane method by considering a linear undamped system with a single degree of freedom described by the equation: $\ddot{r} + \omega_n^2 r = 0$, as well as a linear undamped system with a single degree of freedom with an excitation (see equation [5.1]).

We know that the general solution of the equation:

$$\ddot{r} + \omega_n^2 r = 0$$

is

$$r = C_1 \cos(\omega_n t) + C_2 \sin(\omega_n t),$$

where C_1, C_2 are constants.

Additionally,

$$\dot{r}/\omega_n = -C_1 \sin(\omega_n t) + C_2 \cos(\omega_n t)$$

and therefore:

$$r^2 + (\dot{r}/\omega_n)^2 = C_1^2 + C_2^2 = \text{constant}.$$

The last equation represents in the phase plane a family of concentric circles with a centre at the origin of $\dot{r}/\omega_n, r$ co-ordinates. The radius of each circle is determined from the initial conditions. If the initial conditions are, e.g., for $t = 0$, $r = r_0$ and $\dot{r} = 0$, then $C_2 = 0$ and $C_1 = r_0$, and the circle radius is equal to r_0 because $r^2 + (\dot{r}/\omega_n)^2 = r_0^2$. The solution of the considered equation $\ddot{r} + \omega_n^2 r = 0$ is $r = r_0 \cos(\omega_n t)$ and can be represented by a projection of the vector OA rotating with constant angular velocity on the displacement r co-ordinate axis (see Figure 5.2).

The motion is visualized in the phase plane by a circle trajectory with the beginning of the trajectory at point A_0 (for $t = 0$: $r = r_0$, $\dot{r} = 0$).

The phase-plane method is widely used for solving non-linear problems and is often applied to undamped systems with a single degree of freedom with different excitations or with different inputs.

Let us analyse a simple example of an excitation acting on a linear, undamped system with a single degree of freedom, described by equation [5.1]:

$$m\ddot{r} + kr = e(t) \qquad \text{or} \qquad \ddot{r} + \omega_n^2 r = e(t)/m,$$

where

$$e(t) = F \qquad \text{for } t \geq 0$$

and

$$e(t) = 0 \qquad \text{for } t < 0$$

(and where F is constant) with the initial conditions for $t = 0$: $r = r_0 = 0$, $\dot{r} = \dot{r}_0 = 0$.

The general solution of this equation is:

$$r(t) = F/(m\omega_n^2) + C_1 \cos(\omega_n t) + C_2 \sin(\omega_n t) \qquad \text{for } t \geq 0,$$

where C_1 and C_2 must be determined from the initial conditions.

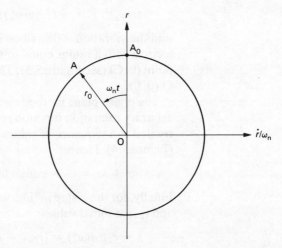

Figure 5.2   Phase-plane diagram for motion of the undamped system defined by equation $\ddot{r} + \omega_n^2 r = 0$ with initial conditions, $t = 0$: $r = r_0$, $\dot{r} = 0$.

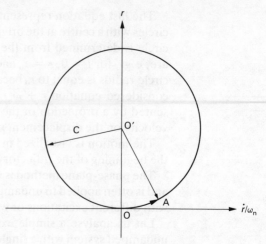

Figure 5.3 Phase-plane diagram for motion of the undamped system with step excitation (initial conditions, $t = 0$: $r = 0$, $\dot{r} = 0$).

From the initial conditions we obtain:

(a) $F/(\omega_n^2 m) + C_1 = 0$ and $C_1 = -F/(m\omega_n^2)$,
(b) $\omega_n C_2 = 0$ and therefore $C_2 = 0$.

Finally,

$$r(t) = F/(m\omega_n^2) - (F/(m\omega_n^2)) \cos(\omega_n t)$$

and

$$\dot{r}(t) = (F\omega_n/(m\omega_n^2)) \sin(\omega_n t).$$

Therefore:

$$(\dot{r}/\omega_n)^2 + [r - (F/(m\omega_n^2))]^2 = (F/(m\omega_n^2))^2 = C^2 = \text{const.}$$

and the vibration is described in the phase plane by a trajectory which is a circle with a radius equal to $C = F/(m\omega_n^2)$ and a centre O′ located at a point $(0, C)$ (see Figure 5.3). The beginning of the trajectory is at the point O $(0, 0)$.

The phase-plane method can be applied to an arbitrary excitation. The arbitrary excitation function $e(t)$, given, e.g., in a graphical form, can be treated as a sequence of values, constant for the duration of the time step (Figure 5.4). Hence:

$$m\ddot{r} + kr = e_k = \text{const. for } t_{k-1} \leqslant t \leqslant t_k. \qquad [5.8]$$

Finally, for the k-step in time we can find the solution of [5.8] treating $\dot{r}_{k-1}$ and r_{k-1} as initial values:

$$r - e_k/(m\omega_n^2) = [r_{k-1} - e_k/(m\omega_n^2)] \cos[\omega_n(t - t_{k-1})]$$
$$+ (\dot{r}_{k-1}/\omega_n) \sin[\omega_n(t - t_{k-1})] \quad \text{for } t_{k-1} \leqslant t \leqslant t_k.$$
$$[5.9]$$

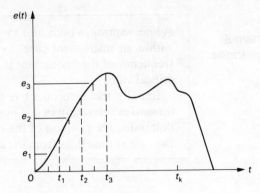

Figure 5.4 Arbitrary excitation function.

Additionally,

$$\dot{r}/\omega_n = -[r_{k-1} - e_k/(m\omega_n^2)] \sin [\omega_n(t - t_{k-1})]$$
$$+ (\dot{r}_{k-1}/\omega_n) \cos [\omega_n(t - t_{k-1})] \qquad \text{for } t_{k-1} \leq t \leq t_k.$$

[5.10]

The formulae [5.9], [5.10] give the possibility of solving the problem numerically step by step.

Finally, squaring equations [5.9], [5.10] and adding them, one obtains:

$$(\dot{r}/\omega_n)^2 + [r - e_k/(m\omega_n^2)]^2$$
$$= (\dot{r}_{k-1}/\omega_n)^2 + [r_{k-1} - e_k/(m\omega_n^2)]^2 = R_k^2 \qquad \text{for } t_{k-1} \leq t \leq t_k.$$

[5.11]

The equation [5.11] enables us also to obtain results in the phase plane by a purely graphical method (see Figure 5.5). In the $(\dot{r}/\omega_n, r)$ plane the motion can be described by a sequence of circular arcs, the so-called phase trajectory.

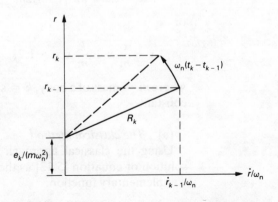

Figure 5.5 Phase-plane trajectory for use in step-by-step solution.

**Example 5.1
Classical, Duhamel
and Laplace methods**

A linear spring, a body and a viscous damper are connected in series within an instrument case, as shown in Figure 5.6. The damped frequency of the instrument is 1 Hz, and the damping is 0.25 of the critical value.

Initially the instrument is at rest. It is then given a constant upward acceleration of 1.2 m/s². By working from first principles, determine the position of the body relative to its initial position in the case at time 0.5 s from the commencement of the motion.

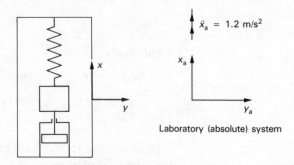

Figure 5.6   Diagram for Example 5.1.

Solution   1.   Let us introduce an appropriate system of co-ordinates associated with the case (Figure 5.6) and let us determine the position of the body (x co-ordinate) relative to its initial position in the case.

When the instrument has a constant upward acceleration in the laboratory system (fixed in space) (in the case under consideration this is 1.2 m/s²) the motion of the body is described in the co-ordinate system connected with the case by the equation:

$$m\ddot{x} + c\dot{x} + kx = -1.2m \qquad [5.12]$$

or

$$\ddot{x} + \frac{c}{m}\dot{x} + \frac{k}{m}x = -1.2, \qquad [5.13]$$

where m = mass of a body, k = spring stiffness and c = viscous damping constant.

(a)   *The classical method*
Using the classical approach we can find immediately a complete solution of equation [5.13] as the sum of the particular integral and the complementary function:

$$x = \exp\{-ct/(2m)\}[C_1 \cos(\omega_d t) + C_2 \sin(\omega_d t)] - 1.2m/k$$

or

$$x = e^{-\xi\omega_n t}[C_1 \cos (\omega_d t) + C_2 \sin (\omega_d t)] - \frac{1.2m}{k},$$

where

$$\omega_d = \omega_n \sqrt{(1 - \xi^2)} = \sqrt{\left(\frac{k}{m} - \frac{c^2}{4m^2}\right)}$$

is the damped circular (angular) natural frequency and ξ is the damping ratio. The C_1, C_2 constants are determined from the initial conditions. Initially the instrument is at rest, therefore for

$$t = 0, \quad x = 0 \quad \text{and} \quad \dot{x} = 0. \qquad [5.14]$$

Hence:

(a) $C_1 = 1.2m/k$, because $x = 0$ at $t = 0$.
(b) $\dot{x} = e^{-ct/(2m)}[-\omega_d C_1 \sin (\omega_d t) + \omega_d C_2 \cos (\omega_d t)]$
$\quad - \{c/(2m)\}e^{-ct/(2m)}[C_1 \cos (\omega_d t) + C_2 \sin (\omega_d t)] = 0$
$\quad$ at $t = 0$.

From (b) we obtain:

$$-\frac{c}{2m} C_1 + \omega_d C_2 = 0$$

or

$$C_2 = \frac{c}{2m} \frac{1.2m}{k\omega_d} = \frac{1.2c}{2k\omega_d}.$$

Finally,

$$x = e^{-ct/(2m)}\left[1.2 \frac{m}{k} \cos (\omega_d t) + \frac{1.2c}{2k\omega_d} \sin (\omega_d t)\right] - \frac{1.2m}{k}. \qquad [5.15]$$

(b) *Duhamel's method*
The same results can be obtained by applying Duhamel's method (the so-called impulse method). In this chapter Duhamel's method was discussed in relation to equation [5.1], which describes the motion of an undamped system with a single degree of freedom with an excitation. Duhamel's method, as well as the other methods, are obviously applicable also to damped systems.

It can be proved (compare with [5.4]) that the response to the unit impulse force acting on a damped system is:

$$g(t - \tau) = \{e^{-(c/2m)(t-\tau)} \sin [\omega_d (t - \tau)]\}/(m\omega_d),$$

where ω_d is the damped circular frequency of a system, τ is the time at which the excitation impulse is applied, and the response to the arbitrary excitation acting on a system with damping is described by equation [5.3]:

$$r(t) = \int_0^t e(\tau)g(t - \tau) \, d\tau.$$

Therefore, for the considered case ([5.13] with [5.14]) the response x to the force $f(t)$ is:

$$x(t) = \int_0^t f(t)\{e^{-h(t-\tau)} \sin [\omega_d(t - \tau)]/(m\omega_d)\} d\tau, \qquad [5.16]$$

where, in the system connected with the case, f is a force acting on the body while the instrument is given a constant upward acceleration. The force f is equal to $-1.2m$, and

$$h = \frac{c}{2m} \quad \text{and} \quad \omega_d = \left(\frac{k}{m} - \frac{c^2}{4m^2}\right)^{0.5}.$$

Integrating by parts one can prove that:

$$\int_0^t e^{-h(t-\tau)} \sin [\omega_d(t - \tau)] d\tau$$

$$= \frac{e^{-ht}[-h \sin (\omega_d t) - \omega_d \cos (\omega_d t)] + \omega_d}{h^2 + \omega_d^2},$$

where

$$\omega_d^2 + h^2 = \frac{k}{m} = \omega_n^2.$$

Therefore, from equation [5.16],

$$x = (-1.2m)(1/\omega_n^2)\{\omega_d - e^{-ht}[h \sin (\omega_d t) + \omega_d \cos (\omega_d t)]\}/(m\omega_d)$$

or

$$x = e^{-ht}[\{1.2h/(\omega_d \omega_n^2)\} \sin (\omega_d t) + (1.2/\omega_n^2) \cos (\omega_d t)] - 1.2/\omega_n^2$$

and finally,

$$x = \frac{-1.2m}{k} + e^{-(c/2m)t}\{C_1 \cos (\omega_d t) + C_2 \sin (\omega_d t)\},$$

where

$$C_1 = 1.2\frac{m}{k} \quad \text{and} \quad C_2 = \frac{1.2c}{2k\omega_d}.$$

This result is the same as equation [5.15].

(c) *The Laplace method*

The problem considered in the Example 5.1(a) and (b) can be also solved using the Laplace method.

Let us re-write equation [5.13] in the form:

$$\frac{\ddot{x}}{\omega_n^2} + \frac{c}{m}\frac{1}{\omega_n^2}\dot{x} + x + \frac{1.2}{\omega_n^2} = 0, \qquad [5.17]$$

where c is the damping constant, and, as was mentioned in Chapter 2, c relates to ξ, the damping ratio, as $c = 2\xi m\omega_n$.

Let us apply next the Laplace transform to the above differential equation in the variable of t. From definition of the Laplace transform [5.5] we know that:

(i)   The Laplace transform $F(s)$ of a function $x(t)$ is:

$$F(s) = \int_0^\infty e^{-st} x(t) \, dt.$$

(ii)   The Laplace transform of a function $\dot{x}(t)$ is:

$$\int_0^\infty e^{-st} \dot{x}(t) \, dt = \left[x(t) \, e^{-st} \right]_0^\infty + \int_0^\infty s \, e^{-st} x(t) \, dt$$

$$= -x(0) + sF(s).$$

(iii)   Analogously we can obtain:

$$\int_0^\infty e^{-st} \ddot{x}(t) \, dt = \left[e^{-st} \dot{x} \right]_0^\infty + \int_0^\infty s \, e^{-st} \dot{x} \, dt = -\dot{x}(0) + \int_0^\infty s \, e^{-st} \dot{x} \, dt$$

$$= s^2 F(s) - sx(0) - \dot{x}(0).$$

(iv)   Also,

$$\int_0^\infty e^{-st} \alpha \, dt = -\frac{1}{s} \left[\alpha \, e^{-st} \right]_0^\infty = \frac{\alpha}{s},$$

where α is constant. Therefore the differential equation [5.17] is transformed into an algebraic equation in the complex variable s:

$$\frac{1}{\omega_n^2} [s^2 F_r(s) - sx(0) - \dot{x}(0)] + \frac{c}{m} \frac{1}{\omega_n^2} [sF_r(s) - x(0)]$$

$$+ F_r(s) + \frac{1.2}{s\omega_n^2} = 0, \quad [5.18]$$

where $F_r(s)$ is the transform $F(s)$ of the unknown response $x(t)$; it is very often called the response transform.

The algebraic equation [5.18] can be rewritten in a more appropriate form:

$$F_r(s) = \frac{[s + (c/m)]x(0) + \dot{x}(0) - 1.2/s}{[s^2 + (c/m)s + \omega_n^2]}. \quad [5.19]$$

This is called the subsidiary equation. Taking into account the initial conditions (for $t = 0$: $x(0) = 0$ and $\dot{x}(0) = 0$) we obtain finally:

$$F_r(s) = \frac{-1.2}{s[s^2 + (c/m)s + \omega_n^2]}. \quad [5.20]$$

The next step in the Laplace procedure is an inverse transformation performed on the subsidiary equation [5.20] which leads to a solution:

$$x(t) = \mathcal{L}^{-1}[F_r(s)].$$

The response transform $F_r(s)$, [5.20], can be presented in the form:

$$F_r(s) = \frac{-1.2}{s[s^2 + (c/m)s + \omega_n^2]} = \frac{-1.2}{s^3 + s^2(a + b) + sab}$$

$$= \frac{-1.2}{s(s + a)(s + b)},$$

where $a + b = c/m$ and $ab = \omega_n^2 = k/m$. The function $1/[s(s + a)(s + b)]$ can be expanded in partial fractions:

$$\frac{1}{s(s + a)(s + b)} = \frac{A}{s} + \frac{B}{(s + a)} + \frac{C}{(s + b)},$$

where

$$A = \left[\frac{1}{(s + a)(s + b)}\right]_{s=0} = \frac{1}{ab},$$

$$B = \left[\frac{1}{s(s + b)}\right]_{s=-a} = \frac{1}{a(a - b)},$$

$$C = \left[\frac{1}{s(s + a)}\right]_{s=-b} = \frac{1}{b(b - a)}.$$

Hence,

$$x(t) = \frac{-1.2}{ab} \mathcal{L}^{-1}\left[\frac{1}{s}\right] - \frac{1.2}{a(a - b)} \mathcal{L}^{-1}\left[\frac{1}{s + a}\right]$$

$$- \frac{1.2}{b(b - a)} \mathcal{L}^{-1}\left[\frac{1}{s + b}\right]$$

and since

$$\mathcal{L}[e^{-at}] = \frac{1}{s + a}$$

we finally obtain:

$$x(t) = -\frac{1.2}{ab} + \frac{(-1.2)b\ e^{-at} + 1.2a\ e^{-bt}}{ab(a - b)}.$$

This leads to:

$$x(t) = \frac{-1.2m}{k} + e^{-(c/2m)t}\left\{\frac{1.2c}{2k\omega_d} \frac{[e^{i\omega_d} - e^{-i\omega_d}]}{2i}\right.$$

$$\left. + \frac{1.2m}{k} \frac{[e^{i\omega_d} + e^{-i\omega_d}]}{2}\right\}$$

$$= \frac{-1.2m}{k} + e^{-(c/2m)t}\left\{\frac{1.2c}{2k\omega_d} \sin \omega_d t + 1.2\frac{m}{k} \cos \omega_d t\right\}$$

$$= \frac{-1.2m}{k} + e^{-(c/2m)t} \{C_1 \cos \omega_d t + C_2 \sin \omega_d t\}, \qquad [5.21]$$

where

$$C_1 = \frac{1.2m}{k}, \qquad C_2 = \frac{1.2c}{2k\omega_d}$$

and

$$\omega_d = \left(\frac{k}{m} - \frac{c^2}{4m^2} \right)^{0.5} = \omega_n (1 - \xi^2)^{0.5}.$$

2. Let us specify the numerical results.

First, we know that a value of the damping c is 0.25 of the critical value c_{cr}:

$$c = 0.25 c_{cr} = 0.5\sqrt{(mk)} = 0.5m\sqrt{\frac{k}{m}} = 0.5m\omega_n.$$

Also we know that the damped frequency is 1 Hz, i.e. that:

$$\frac{\omega_d}{2\pi} = 1 \qquad \text{and} \qquad \omega_d = 2\pi \ [\text{rad/s}].$$

On the other hand:

$$\omega_d = \sqrt{\left(\frac{k}{m} - \frac{c^2}{4m^2} \right)} = \sqrt{\left(\frac{k}{m} - \frac{k}{m}\frac{0.25m^2}{4m^2} \right)} = \frac{\sqrt{15}}{4}\sqrt{\frac{k}{m}}$$

$$= 0.96825 \sqrt{\left(\frac{k}{m} \right)} \ [\text{rad/s}].$$

Therefore:

$$2\pi = 0.96825 \sqrt{\left(\frac{k}{m} \right)}$$

or

$$\sqrt{\left(\frac{k}{m} \right)} = \frac{2\pi}{0.96825} = 6.4892.$$

$$\frac{k}{m} = 42.1098 \ [\text{rad}^2/\text{s}^2] \qquad \text{or} \qquad \frac{m}{k} = 0.0237.$$

Putting numerical values into the solution [5.15], which describes the position of the body relative to its initial position in the case at $t = 0$, we obtain:

$$x(t) = e^{-0.25\sqrt{(k/m)}t}\left[1.2\,\frac{m}{k}\cos{(2\pi t)} + \frac{1.2 \times 0.5\sqrt{(k/m)}m}{2k \times 2\pi}\sin{(2\pi t)} \right.$$

$$\left. - \frac{m}{k} \times 1.2 \right]$$

or

$$x(t) = e^{-0.25 \times 6.4892t} \left[1.2 \times 0.0237 \cos (2\pi t) \right.$$

$$\left. + \frac{1.2 \times 0.25}{2\pi} 0.0237 \times 6.4892 \times \sin (2\pi t) \right]$$

$$- 1.2 \times 0.0237$$

or

$$x(t) = e^{-1.6223t}[0.0284 \cos (2\pi t) + 7.3431 \times 10^{-3} \sin (2\pi t)]$$
$$- 0.0284.$$

Therefore, the position of the body, relative to its initial position in the case, at time 0.5 s from the commencement of the motion, is:

$$x(0.5) = e^{-1.6223 \times 0.5}[0.0284 \cos \pi] - 0.0284$$
$$= -e^{-0.81115}0.0284 - 0.0284$$
$$= -0.0284(1 + e^{-0.81115})$$
$$= -0.0284(1 + 0.4443) = -0.041 \text{ m} = -41 \text{ mm}.$$

Answer The position of the body relative to the case after 0.5 s is **41 mm** below its initial position in the case.

Example 5.2
Classical, Duhamel and phase-plane methods

A machine of mass 5000 kg rests upon elastic supports which have a total stiffness of 1.5 MN/m, and is initially at rest, see (Figure 5.7(a)). Due to local disturbances, the ground upon which the supports rest is given a vertical displacement y, which varies in time t as shown in Figure 5.7(b).

Estimate the amplitude of free vibration of the machine for time $t \geqslant 0.6$ s. Assume that the machine has one degree of freedom in the vertical direction and that damping is negligible.

Solution Let us consider a co-ordinate system fixed in space (laboratory system) in which Y describes the position of the machine during motion

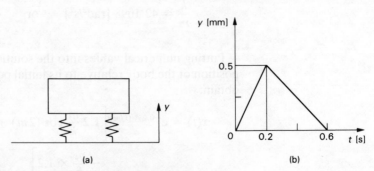

Figure 5.7 Diagram for Example 5.2.

and y describes the ground disturbance. The equation of motion for the machine is:

$$m\ddot{Y} + k(Y - y) = 0, \tag{5.22}$$

where

$$y = 2.5 \times 10^{-3}t \text{ [m]} \qquad \text{for } 0 \le t \le 0.2 \text{ [s]}$$

and

$$y = 0.75 \times 10^{-3} - 1.25 \times 10^{-3}t \text{ [m]} \qquad \text{for } 0.2 \le t \le 0.6 \text{ [s]}$$

and

$$y = 0 \qquad \text{for } t \ge 0.6 \text{ [s]}.$$

The initial conditions (at $t = 0$) are:

$$Y(0) = 0 \qquad \text{and} \qquad \dot{Y}(0) = 0. \tag{5.23}$$

Let us find a solution of [5.22] with the initial conditions [5.23] using two different approaches.

(a) *The classical approach*

We consider separately three ranges of time:
range I   for $0 \le t \le 0.2$,
range II   for $0.2 \le t \le 0.6$,
range III for $t \ge 0.6$.

Let Y_I, Y_{II} and Y_{III} denote solution of [5.22] during ranges I, II and III, respectively.

We shall find the solution of equation [5.22] which satisfies the initial conditions [5.23] and the so-called matching conditions at $t = 0.2$ and at $t = 0.6$.

For $t = 0.2$

$$Y_I(0.2) = Y_{II}(0.2)$$

and

$$\dot{Y}_I(0.2) = \dot{Y}_{II}(0.2).$$

The matching conditions are nothing more than initial conditions for the equation of motion in range II of time, at $t = 0.2$.

For $t = 0.6$ the matching conditions are:

$$Y_{II}(0.6) = Y_{III}(0.6)$$

and

$$\dot{Y}_{II}(0.6) = \dot{Y}_{III}(0.6).$$

(i)   In range I ($0 \le t \le 0.2$) the general or complete solution of [5.22] is:

$$Y_I(t) = A_1 \cos (\omega_n t) + B_1 \sin (\omega_n t) + 2.5 \times 10^{-3}t,$$

where

$$\omega_n = (k/m)^{0.5}$$

and $A_1 \, B_1$ are constants which are determined from the initial conditions at $t = 0$:

$$Y_I(0) = A_1 = 0 \quad \text{and} \quad \dot{Y}_I(0) = \omega_n B_1 + 2.5 \times 10^{-3} = 0.$$

Therefore:

$$A_1 = 0 \quad \text{and} \quad B_1 = -2.5 \times 10^{-3}/\omega_n$$

and finally

$$Y_I(t) = (-2.5 \times 10^{-3}/\omega_n) \sin(\omega_n t) + 2.5 \times 10^{-3} t. \qquad [5.24]$$

   (ii)   During range II the complete solution is:

$$\begin{aligned} Y_{II}(t) = &(-2.5 \times 10^{-3}/\omega_n) \sin(\omega_n t) + A_2 \cos[\omega_n(t - 0.2)] \\ &+ B_2 \sin[\omega_n(t - 0.2)] + 0.75 \times 10^{-3} - 1.25 \times 10^{-3} t, \end{aligned}$$

where A_2, B_2 are constants which are determined from the matching conditions at $t = 0.2$:

$$Y_I(0.2) = Y_{II}(0.2) \quad \text{and} \quad \dot{Y}_I(0.2) = \dot{Y}_{II}(0.2).$$

Therefore, for $t = 0.2$,

$$\begin{aligned} (-2.5 &\times 10^{-3}/\omega_n) \sin(0.2\omega_n) + 0.5 \times 10^{-3} \\ &= (-2.5 \times 10^{-3}/\omega_n) \sin(0.2\omega_n) + A_2 + 0.5 \times 10^{-3} \end{aligned}$$

and

$$\begin{aligned} \omega_n(-2.5 &\times 10^{-3}/\omega_n) \cos(0.2\omega_n) + 2.5 \times 10^{-3} \\ &= \omega_n(-2.5 \times 10^{-3}/\omega_n) \cos(0.2\omega_n) + \omega_n \times B_2 - 1.25 \times 10^{-3}. \end{aligned}$$

Hence

$$A_2 = 0 \quad \text{and} \quad \omega_n B_2 = 3.75 \times 10^{-3}$$

or

$$A_2 = 0 \quad \text{and} \quad B_2 = 3.75 \times 10^{-3}/\omega_n.$$

Therefore:

$$\begin{aligned} Y_{II}(t) = &(-2.5 \times 10^{-3}/\omega_n) \sin(\omega_n t) \\ &+ (3.75 \times 10^{-3}/\omega_n) \sin[\omega_n(t - 0.2)] \\ &+ (0.75 - 1.25t) \times 10^{-3} \quad \text{for} \quad 0.2 \le t \le 0.6. \end{aligned}$$
$$[5.25]$$

   (iii)   Finally for $t \ge 0.6$ the complete solution of [5.22] is:

$$\begin{aligned} Y_{III}(t) = &B_1 \sin(\omega_n t) + B_2 \sin[\omega_n(t - 0.2)] \\ &+ A_3 \cos[\omega_n(t - 0.6)] + B_3 \sin[\omega_n(t - 0.6)] \end{aligned}$$

or

$$\begin{aligned} Y_{III}(t) = &(-2.5 \times 10^{-3}/\omega_n) \sin(\omega_n t) + (3.75 \times 10^{-3}/\omega_n) \\ &\times \sin[\omega_n(t - 0.2)] + A_3 \cos[\omega_n(t - 0.6)] \\ &+ B_3 \sin[\omega_n(t - 0.6)], \end{aligned}$$

where A_3, B_3 are constants which are determined from the matching conditions at $t = 0.6$:

$$Y_{II}(0.6) = Y_{III}(0.6),$$
$$\dot{Y}_{II}(0.6) = \dot{Y}_{III}(0.6)$$

or

$$(-2.5 \times 10^{-3}/\omega_n) \sin (0.6\omega_n) + (3.75 \times 10^{-3}/\omega_n) \sin (0.4\omega_n)$$
$$= (-2.5 \times 10^{-3}/\omega_n) \sin (0.6\omega_n) + (3.75 \times 10^{-3}/\omega_n)$$
$$\times \sin (0.4\omega_n) + A_3$$

and

$$(-2.5 \times 10^{-3}) \cos (0.6\omega_n) + 3.75 \times 10^{-3} \cos (0.4\omega_n)$$
$$- 1.25 \times 10^{-3}$$
$$= (-2.5 \times 10^{-3}) \cos (0.6\omega_n) + 3.75 \times 10^{-3} \cos (0.4\omega_n)$$
$$+ \omega_n B_3.$$

Hence:

$$A_3 = 0 \quad \text{and} \quad B_3 = (-1.25 \times 10^{-3})/\omega_n.$$

Therefore for $t \geqslant 0.6$:

$$Y_{III}(t) = (-2.5 \times 10^{-3}/\omega_n) \sin (\omega_n t)$$
$$+ (3.75 \times 10^{-3}/\omega_n) \sin [\omega_n(t - 0.2)]$$
$$+ (-1.25 \times 10^{-3}/\omega_n) \sin [\omega_n(t - 0.6)]. \qquad [5.26]$$

Finally, we can calculate the amplitude of free vibration of the machine for time $t \geqslant 0.6$:

$$Y_{III}(t) = (-2.5 \times 10^{-3}/\omega_n) \sin (\omega_n t) + (3.75 \times 10^{-3}/\omega_n) \sin (\omega_n t)$$
$$\times \cos (0.2\omega_n) + (-3.75 \times 10^{-3}/\omega_n) \sin (0.2\omega_n) \cos (\omega_n t)$$
$$- (1.25 \times 10^{-3}/\omega_n) \cos (0.6\omega_n) \sin (\omega_n t)$$
$$+ (1.25 \times 10^{-3}/\omega_n) \sin (0.6\omega_n) \cos (\omega_n t).$$

$$Y_{III}(t) = [-2.5 \times 10^{-3}/\omega_n + (3.75 \times 10^{-3}/\omega_n) \cos (0.2\omega_n)$$
$$- (1.25 \times 10^{-3}/\omega_n) \cos (0.6\omega_n)] \sin (\omega_n t)$$
$$+ [-(3.75 \times 10^{-3}/\omega_n) \sin (0.2\omega_n)$$
$$+ (1.25 \times 10^{-3}/\omega_n) \sin (0.6\omega_n)] \cos (\omega_n t)$$

or

$$Y_{III}(t) = (10^{-3}/\omega_n)\{[-2.5 + 3.75 \cos (0.2\omega_n) - 1.25 \cos (0.6\omega_n)]$$
$$\times \sin (\omega_n t) + [-3.75 \sin (0.2\omega_n)$$
$$+ 1.25 \sin (0.6\omega_n)] \cos (\omega_n t)\}$$

and the amplitude C of free vibration of the machine for time $t \geqslant 0.6$ is:

$$C = (10^{-3}/\omega_n)\{[-2.5 + 3.75 \cos (0.2\omega_n) - 1.25 \cos (0.6\omega_n)]^2$$
$$+ [-3.75 \sin (0.2\omega_n) + 1.25 \sin (0.6\omega_n)]^2\}^{0.5}.$$

We know that $k/m = \omega_n^2 = 300$ and $\omega_n = 17.32$, $(1/\omega_n) = 0.05774$.

Therefore:

$$C = 10^{-3} \times 0.05774 \times \{[-2.5 + 3.75 \cos (0.2 \times 17.32)$$
$$- 1.25 \cos (0.6 \times 17.32)]^2$$
$$+ [-3.75 \sin (0.2 \times 17.32)$$
$$+ 1.25 \sin (0.6 \times 17.32)]^2\}^{0.5}$$
$$= 10^{-3} \times 0.05774 \times \{[-2.5 - 3.75 \cos (0.3224)$$
$$+ 1.25 \cos (0.9672)]^2$$
$$+ [3.75 \sin (0.3224)$$
$$- 1.25 \sin (0.9672)]^2\}^{0.5}$$
$$= 10^{-3} \times 0.05774 \times \{[-2.5 - 3.5568 + 1.25 \times 0.5676]^2$$
$$+ [1.188 - 1.25 \times 0.8233]^2\}^{0.5}$$
$$= 10^{-3} \times 0.05774 \times \{28.5936 + 0.0252\}^{0.5}$$
$$= 10^{-3} \times 0.05774 \times 5.3497 = 0.31 \times 10^{-3} \text{m}.$$

Therefore, $C = 0.31$ mm, i.e., that the amplitude of free vibration of the machine for time $t \geq 0.6$ s amounts to 0.31 mm.

(b)   *Duhamel's integral method*
The same results may be obtained by Duhamel's integral method (so-called impulse method).

The response to the excitation due to a ground disturbance is for the considered case (equation [5.22] and the initial conditions [5.23]):

$$Y = \int_0^t [ky/(m\omega_n)] \sin [\omega_n(t - \tau)] \, d\tau, \qquad [5.27]$$

where ω_n is the angular (circular) natural frequency of the system.

As in the classical approach, we consider separately three ranges of time: $0 \leq t \leq 0.2, 0.2 \leq t \leq 0.6$, and $t \geq 0.6$.

For $t \geq 0.6$ the response to the considered ground disturbance can be presented as follows:

$$Y(t) = \int_0^{0.2} [ky/(m\omega_n)] \sin [\omega_n(t - \tau)] \, d\tau$$

$$+ \int_{0.2}^{0.6} [ky/(m\omega_n)] \sin [\omega_n(t - \tau)] \, d\tau$$

$$+ \int_{0.6}^t [ky/(m\omega_n)] \sin [\omega_n(t - \tau)] \, d\tau, \qquad [5.28]$$

where

$$y = 2.5 \times 10^{-3}\tau \qquad \text{for } 0 \leq \tau \leq 0.2,$$
$$y = 10^{-3} \times (0.75 - 1.25\tau) \qquad \text{for } 0.2 \leq \tau \leq 0.6,$$

and

$$y = 0 \qquad \text{for } \tau \geq 0.6.$$

Hence for $t \geqslant 0.6$

$$Y(t) = \int_0^{0.2} [2.5 \times 10^{-3}\tau/(m\omega_n)] \sin [\omega_n(t - \tau)] \, d\tau$$

$$+ \int_{0.2}^{0.6} [10^{-3} \times (0.75 - 1.25\tau)/(m\omega_n)] \sin [\omega_n(t - \tau)] \, d\tau.$$

$$[5.29]$$

We can obtain finally from [5.29] the amplitude of free vibration of the machine for $t \geqslant 0.6$.

However, for a comparison of both methods, Duhamel's integral method with the classical approach, let us analyse a solution in the various time ranges:

(i) In the time range I $(0 \leqslant t \leqslant 0.2)$, the solution of [5.22] with the initial conditions [5.23] is:

$$Y_I(t) = k \int_0^t [2.5 \times 10^{-3}\tau/(m\omega_n)] \sin [\omega_n(t - \tau)] \, d\tau.$$

But

$$\int_0^t \tau \sin [\omega_n(t - \tau)] \, d\tau$$

$$= \int_0^t (\omega_n/\omega_n)\tau \sin [\omega_n(t - \tau)] \, d\tau$$

$$= \left[(\tau/\omega_n) \cos [\omega_n(t - \tau)] \right]_0^t - \int_0^t \cos [\omega_n(t - \tau)]/\omega_n \, d\tau$$

$$= \left[(\tau/\omega_n) \cos [\omega_n(t - \tau)] \right]_0^t - \int_0^t (\omega_n/\omega_n^2) \cos [\omega_n(t - \tau)] \, d\tau$$

$$= \left[(\tau/\omega_n) \cos [\omega_n(t - \tau)] \right]_0^t + \left[(1/\omega_n^2) \sin [\omega_n(t - \tau)] \right]_0^t$$

$$= (t/\omega_n) - (1/\omega_n^2) \sin (\omega_n t),$$

where $\omega_n = (k/m)^{0.5}$. Therefore

$$Y_I(t) = [k/(m\omega_n)] \times 2.5 \times 10^{-3}[(t/\omega_n) - (1/\omega_n^2) \sin (\omega_n t)]$$
$$= 2.5 \times 10^{-3}kt/(m\omega_n^2) - [2.5 \times 10^{-3}k/(m\omega_n^3)] \sin (\omega_n t)$$

or

$$Y_I(t) = y + B_1 \sin (\omega_n t),$$

where

$$B_1 = -2.5 \times 10^{-3}/\omega_n, \qquad y = 2.5 \times 10^{-3}t,$$

the same results as for the classical approach (see equation [5.24]).

(ii) In range II $(0.2 \leqslant t \leqslant 0.6)$, the solution is:

$$Y_{II}(t) = \int_0^{0.2} 2.5 \times 10^{-3} k\tau/(m\omega_n) \sin [\omega_n(t - \tau)] \, d\tau$$

$$+ \int_{0.2}^t [10^{-3}k/(m\omega_n)](0.75 - 1.25\tau) \sin [\omega_n(t - \tau)] \, d\tau$$

$$= 2.5 \times 10^{-3}\omega_n \int_0^{0.2} \tau \sin [\omega_n(t - \tau)] \, d\tau$$

$$+ 0.75 \times 10^{-3}\omega_n \int_{0.2}^t \sin [\omega_n(t - \tau)] \, d\tau$$

$$- 1.25 \times 10^{-3}\omega_n \int_{0.2}^t \tau \sin [\omega_n(t - \tau)] \, d\tau$$

$$= 2.5 \times 10^{-3}\omega_n \left[(1/\omega_n)\tau \cos [\omega_n(t - \tau)] \right]_0^{0.2}$$

$$+ 2.5 \times 10^{-3} \left[(1/\omega_n) \sin [\omega_n(t - \tau)] \right]_0^{0.2}$$

$$+ 0.75 \times 10^{-3} \int_{0.2}^t \omega_n \sin [\omega_n(t - \tau)] \, d\tau$$

$$- 1.25 \times 10^{-3}\omega_n \int_{0.2}^t \tau(\omega_n/\omega_n) \sin [\omega_n(t - \tau)] \, d\tau.$$

Therefore:

$$Y_{II}(t) = 2.5 \times 10^{-3}\{0.2 \cos [\omega_n(t - 0.2)] + (1/\omega_n) \sin [\omega_n(t - 0.2)] - (1/\omega_n) \sin (\omega_n t)\}$$

$$+ 0.75 \times 10^{-3} \left[\cos [\omega_n(t - \tau)] \right]_{0.2}^t$$

$$- 1.25 \times 10^{-3} \left[\tau \cos [\omega_n(t - \tau)] \right]_{0.2}^t$$

$$- 1.25 \times 10^{-3} \left[(1/\omega_n) \sin [\omega_n(t - \tau)] \right]_{0.2}^t$$

and finally,

$$Y_{II}(t) = 0.5 \times 10^{-3} \cos [\omega_n(t - 0.2)]$$
$$+ (2.5 \times 10^{-3}/\omega_n) \sin [\omega_n(t - 0.2)]$$
$$- (2.5 \times 10^{-3}/\omega_n) \sin (\omega_n t)$$
$$+ 0.75 \times 10^{-3}\{1 - \cos [\omega_n(t - 0.2)]\} - 1.25 \times 10^{-3}t$$
$$+ 1.25 \times 10^{-3} \times 0.2 \cos [\omega_n(t - 0.2)] - (1.25 \times 10^{-3}/\omega_n)$$

$$\times \left[\sin [\omega_n(t - \tau)] \right]_{0.2}^t.$$

Therefore,

$$Y_{II}(t) = \{0.5 - 0.75 + 1.25 \times 0.2\} \times 10^{-3} \cos[\omega_n(t - 0.2)]$$
$$+ 10^{-3}\{2.5/\omega_n + 1.25/\omega_n\} \sin[\omega_n(t - 0.2)]$$
$$- (2.5 \times 10^{-3}/\omega_n) \sin(\omega_n t) + 0.75 \times 10^{-3}$$
$$- 1.25 \times 10^{-3}t.$$

Finally, we obtain:

$$Y_{II}(t) = (-2.5 \times 10^{-3}/\omega_n) \sin(\omega_n t)$$
$$+ (3.75/\omega_n) \times 10^{-3} \sin[\omega_n(t - 0.2)]$$
$$+ (0.75 - 1.25t)10^{-3},$$

which is in agreement with the result, [5.25], obtained by the classical method.

For time $t \geq 0.6$, $y = 0$ and therefore equation [5.28] can be simplified to:

$$Y_{III}(t) = \int_0^{0.2} ky/(m\omega_n) \sin[\omega_n(t - \tau)] \, d\tau$$

$$+ \int_{0.2}^{0.6} ky/(m\omega_n) \sin[\omega_n(t - \tau)] \, d\tau$$

$$= \int_0^{0.2} [2.5 \times 10^{-3}k\tau/(m\omega_n)] \sin[\omega_n(t - \tau)] \, d\tau$$

$$+ \int_{0.2}^{0.6} [0.75 \times 10^{-3}k/(m\omega_n)] \sin[\omega_n(t - \tau)] \, d\tau$$

$$- \int_{0.2}^{0.6} [1.25 \times 10^{-3}k\tau/(m\omega_n)] \sin[\omega_n(t - \tau)] \, d\tau.$$

$$Y_{III}(t) = 2.5 \times 10^{-3}\omega_n\{(0.2/\omega_n) \cos[\omega_n(t - 0.2)]$$
$$+ (1/\omega_n^2) \sin[\omega_n(t - 0.2)]$$
$$- (1/\omega_n^2) \sin(\omega_n t)\}$$

$$+ 0.75 \times 10^{-3}\left[\cos[\omega_n(t - \tau)]\right]_{0.2}^{0.6}$$

$$- 1.25 \times 10^{-3}\omega_n\{(0.6/\omega_n) \cos[\omega_n(t - 0.6)]$$
$$- (0.2/\omega_n) \cos[\omega_n(t - 0.2)]$$
$$+ (1/\omega_n^2) \sin[\omega_n(t - 0.6)]$$
$$- (1/\omega_n^2) \sin[\omega_n(t - 0.2)]\}.$$

Finally,

$$Y_{III}(t) = 0.5 \times 10^{-3} \cos[\omega_n(t - 0.2)]$$
$$+ (2.5 \times 10^{-3}/\omega_n) \sin[\omega_n(t - 0.2)]$$
$$- (2.5 \times 10^{-3}/\omega_n) \sin(\omega_n t)$$
$$+ 0.75 \times 10^{-3} \cos[\omega_n(t - 0.6)]$$
$$- 0.75 \times 10^{-3} \cos[\omega_n(t - 0.2)]$$
$$- 0.75 \times 10^{-3} \cos[\omega_n(t - 0.6)]$$
$$+ 0.25 \times 10^{-3} \cos[\omega_n(t - 0.2)]$$
$$- (1.25 \times 10^{-3}/\omega_n) \sin[\omega_n(t - 0.6)]$$
$$+ (1.25 \times 10^{-3}/\omega_n) \sin[\omega_n(t - 0.2)]$$

or

$$Y_{III}(t) = (-2.5 \times 10^{-3}/\omega_n) \sin (\omega_n t)$$
$$+ (3.75 \times 10^{-3}/\omega_n) \sin [\omega_n(t - 0.2)]$$
$$- (1.25 \times 10^{-3}/\omega_n) \sin [\omega_n(t - 0.6)],$$

which is the same as equation [5.26] from the classical method.

(iii) *The phase-plane method*

Example 5.2 may be solved by using the phase-plane method. The trajectory in the phase plane is normally, in a practical approach, most easily obtained by a graphical technique. However, the equation of the trajectory in the phase plane may be established analytically. Let us firstly obtain the exact trajectory describing the motion (Example 5.2), and let us secondly find the approximate trajectory by the graphical technique and compare both results.

The general solution of motion described by equation [5.22] is:

$$Y = A \cos (\omega_n t) + B \sin (\omega_n t) + y, \qquad [5.30]$$

where in general $y = \beta + \alpha t$, with α, β as constants. The solution, [5.30], may be written in the form:

$$Y = C \sin (\omega_n t + \Phi) + \alpha t + \beta, \qquad [5.31]$$

where C, Φ are constants determined from the initial conditions, and where $C^2 = A^2 + B^2$ and $\tan \Phi = A/B$.

Therefore:

$$\dot{Y}/\omega_n = C \cos (\omega_n t + \Phi) + (\alpha/\omega_n). \qquad [5.32]$$

Hence we can deduce from [5.31] and [5.32] that in the co-ordinate system $\dot{Y}/\omega_n$, Y (the phase plane) the considered motion is described by a cycloid:

$$Y = at' - a\lambda \sin t' + b,$$
$$\dot{Y}/\omega_n = a - a\lambda \cos t',$$

where $a = \alpha/\omega_n, t' = \omega_n t + \Phi$ and

$$\lambda = -\omega_n C/\alpha = -\omega_n(A^2 + B^2)^{0.5}/\alpha,$$
$$b = \beta - \alpha\Phi/\omega_n, \qquad \Phi = \arctan (A/B).$$

We know that:

$$y = 2.5 \times 10^{-3}t \qquad \text{for } 0 \leqslant t \leqslant 0.2 \text{ (range I)},$$
$$y = 0.75 \times 10^{-3} - 1.25 \times 10^{-3}t \qquad \text{for } 0.2 \leqslant t \leqslant 0.6 \text{ (range II)},$$
$$\text{and } y = 0 \qquad \text{for } t \geqslant 0.6 \text{ (range III)}.$$

Hence, considering the initial conditions, we can deduce from [5.31] and [5.32] that:

$$\text{for } 0 \leqslant t \leqslant 0.2 \quad a = \alpha/\omega_n = 2.5 \times 10^{-3}/17.32 = 0.144 \times 10^{-3},$$
$$t' = \omega_n t = 17.32t, \qquad \lambda = -C\omega_n/\alpha = 1,$$
$$\Phi = 0 \qquad \text{and} \qquad b = 0.$$

Analogously, for $0.2 \leqslant t \leqslant 0.6$:

$$a = \alpha/\omega_n = (-1.25 \times 10^{-3})/17.32 = -0.07217 \times 10^{-3},$$
$$t' = \omega_n t + \Phi = 17.32t + \Phi,$$
$$\Phi = \arctan(A/B) = (\pi - 0.19370) \text{ [rad]},$$
$$b = \beta - \alpha\Phi/\omega_n = 0.96275 \times 10^{-3},$$
$$\lambda = -\omega_n C/\alpha = 4.96.$$

Finally, for $t \geqslant 0.6$, $y = 0$, and the motion is described in the phase plane by a circle with a centre at the origin of the co-ordinate system $(0, 0)$:

$$Y^2 + (\dot{Y}/\omega_n)^2 = A^2 + B^2 = C^2 = \text{constant} = (0.3103 \times 10^{-3})^2.$$

The analytical trajectory in the phase plane is presented in Figure 5.8 and

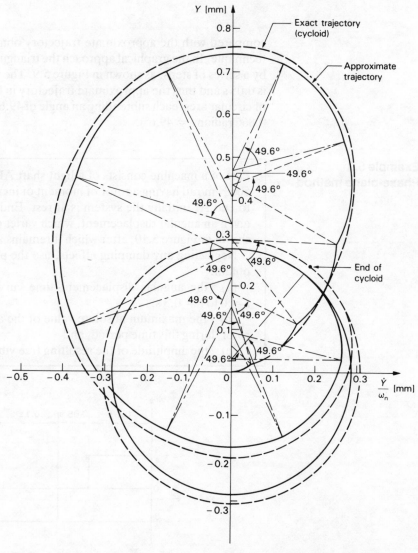

Figure 5.8 Exact and approximate trajectories in the phase plane (Example 5.2).

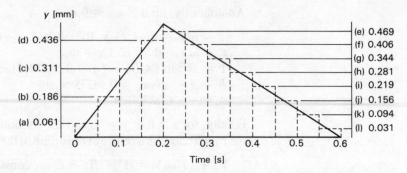

Figure 5.9 Triangular excitation function (Example 5.2) represented approximately by a series of steps.

compared with the approximate trajectory obtained using the graphical technique. In the graphical approach the triangular pulse is approximated by a series of steps, as shown in Figure 5.9. The time interval of each step is 0.05 s and thus the approximate trajectory in the phase plane is a series of circular arcs, each subtending an angle of 49.6° ($\omega_n t = 17.32 \times 0.05 = 0.866$ radians $= 49.6°$).

Example 5.3
Phase-plane method

Part of a machine consists of a light shaft AB of torsional stiffness 500 N m/rad having a rotor of moment of inertia 1.1 kg m² attached to end A. Initially the system is at rest. End B of the shaft is then given an angular displacement, which varies over a time of 0.25 s as shown in Figure 5.10, after which it remains at rest.

Neglecting any damping effects, use the phase-plane method to obtain:

(a) the angular displacement–time curve for the rotor from $t = 0$ to $t = 0.3$ s,

(b) the maximum absolute value of the angular velocity of the rotor during this time period, and

(c) the amplitude of the resulting free vibration of the rotor.

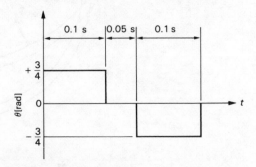

Figure 5.10 Diagram for Example 5.3.

Solution   The equation of motion for the rotor at A is:

$$I_A \ddot{\theta}_A = -S(\theta_A - \theta),$$

where I_A is the moment of inertia of the rotor ($= 1.1 \text{ kg m}^2$), S is the torsional stiffness of the shaft AB ($= 500 \text{ N m/rad}$), θ_A is the angular displacement of the rotor at A and θ is the angular displacement of end B of the shaft. This equation may be written as:

$$\ddot{\theta}_A + \omega_n^2 \theta_A = \omega_n^2 \theta, \qquad [5.33]$$

where ω_n is the undamped circular natural frequency and

$$\omega_n = (S/I_A)^{0.5} = (500/1.1)^{0.5} = 21.32 \text{ rad/s}.$$

Initially the system is at rest; thus for $t = 0$, $\theta_A = \dot{\theta}_A = 0$.

It should be noted that the angular displacement of end B has constant values in the appropriate time ranges. Therefore, we can introduce a variable $\psi_A = \theta_A - \theta$ and hence equation [5.33] becomes:

$$\ddot{\psi}_A = -\omega_n^2 \psi_A. \qquad [5.34]$$

Additionally, a new variable can be defined:

$$\phi_A = \dot{\psi}_A. \qquad [5.35]$$

Hence,

$$\dot{\phi}_A = -\omega_n^2 \psi_A. \qquad [5.36]$$

Equations [5.35] and [5.36] are equivalent to equation [5.34]. From [5.35] and [5.36] we can deduce:

$$\frac{d\phi_A}{d\psi_A} = -\omega_n^2(\psi_A/\phi_A)$$

or

$$\phi_A \, d\phi_A = -\omega_n^2 \psi_A \, d\psi_A. \qquad [5.37]$$

Integration of both sides of equation [5.37] leads to:

$$\phi_A^2/\omega_n^2 + \psi_A^2 = \text{constant}$$

or

$$\theta_A^2/\omega_n^2 + (\theta_A - \theta)^2 = \text{constant}. \qquad [5.38]$$

From the initial conditions (for $t = 0$) we can determine the value of the constant in equation [5.38], namely:

$$\text{constant} = \theta_0^2 = 0.75^2$$

because

$$\theta = \theta_0 = 0.75 \text{ rad} \qquad \text{for } 0 \leq t \leq 0.1.$$

Finally,

$$\dot{\theta}_A^2/\omega_n^2 + (\theta_A - \theta)^2 = \theta_0^2 \qquad [5.39]$$

and this equation describes motion of the rotor in the phase plane

$(\dot{\theta}_A/\omega_n, \theta_A)$. In this case the trajectory of motion is a circle of radius θ_0 with the circle centre at point $(0, \theta)$ (compare with Figure 5.3).

Equation [5.39] enables the trajectory in the phase plane to be constructed when the input is a series of steps. We should also note that the constant in equation [5.38] (or θ_0^2 in equation [5.39]) has different values for different excitations, i.e., various values in various time ranges. As was proved previously, we can easily determine this constant for $0 \leqslant t \leqslant 0.1$ s. However, the further procedure to find θ_0^2 for $t \geqslant 0.1$ requests values of $\theta_A (0.1)$, $\dot{\theta}_A (0.1)$ as well as $\theta (0.1)$. In the classical approach it would be equivalent to determining a solution step by step using matching conditions. In the graphical phase-plane method a knowledge of θ_0^2 is necessary only for the first step of the input and, in the considered case, θ_0 is a value of the radius of the circle which is the motion trajectory. For the next step of the input (in the considered case, the excitation is equal to 0) the centre of the new circle is at the point $(0, \theta)$ (in this case at $(0, 0)$).

The radius of the new circle can be easily found graphically because $\theta_A (0.1)$ and $\dot{\theta}_A (0.1)$ are also known (Figure 5.11).

Let us analyse in detail the graphical phase-plane method. In the present example $\theta = \theta_0 = 0.75$ rad for $0 \leqslant t \leqslant 0.1$ s, so we can construct as a trajectory an arc of a circle which subtends an angle of $\omega_n \times 0.1 = 2.132$ rad or $122.2°$. Thus, in the phase plane, shown in Figure 5.11, an arc

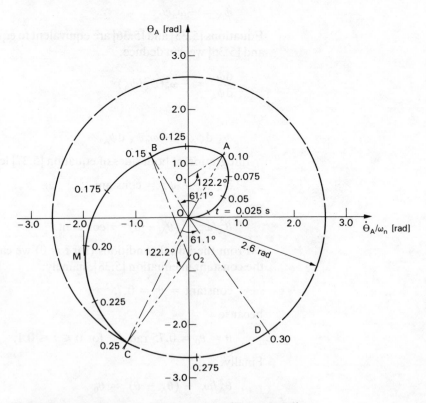

Figure 5.11 Trajectory in the phase plane (Example 5.3).

of a circle with centre at O_1 (co-ordinates: 0, 0.75) is drawn from O to A such that angle OO_1A is 122.2°. For the next 0.05 s the excitation is zero (see Figure 5.10), thus in the phase plane an arc AB of a circle with centre at O (0, 0) is drawn, so that the arc AB subtends an angle of 61.1°. Finally, an arc BC of circle (centre O_2 (0, −0.75)) is constructed with angle BO_2C = 122.2°. For $t > 0.25$ s the excitation is zero and the motion trajectory in the phase plane is a circle with the centre O (0, 0), and the radius OC.

The measured value of the radius OC (Figure 5.11) amounts to **2.6 rad** and this is the amplitude of the resulting free vibration (answer to part (c)).

The maximum absolute value of the angular velocity during the time period from $t = 0$ to $t = 0.3$ s is obtained as the maximum absolute value of the $\dot{\theta}/\omega_n$ co-ordinate reached by the trajectory during this time period. This occurs at about M where $\dot{\theta}_A/\omega_n = -2.0$, and therefore the maximum of the absolute value of angular velocity is 42.6 rad/s.

Answer to part (b)   Maximum absolute angular velocity is **42.6 rad/s.**

To draw the angular displacement–time curve we need to mark on the motion trajectory in the phase plane the points at intervals of time, say, 0.025 s and to find (Figure 5.11) values of θ_A which refer to these points. Thus, for example, at 0.075 s the displacement θ_A is 0.78 rad, at $t = 0.125$ s, $\theta_A = 1.32$ rad, and when $t = 0.225$ s, $\theta_A = -1.52$ rad. In this manner the angular displacement–time curve, Figure 5.12, may be drawn.

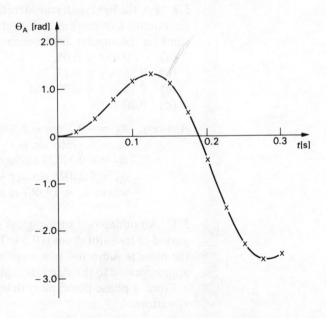

Figure 5.12   Angular displacement against time obtained from Figure 5.11.

Problems

5.1 A light shaft, supported in bearings where friction is negligible, carries a rotor at one end and a pinion at the other. The natural frequency of vibration of the system is 2.78 Hz.

The system is initially at rest when the pinion is given a series of step displacements, as shown in Figure 5.13. Using the phase-plane method, determine the amplitude of the residual free vibration, and sketch the curve of displacement against time.

Answer 0.30 rad.

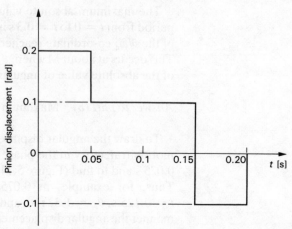

Figure 5.13   Diagram for Problems 5.1 and 5.2.

5.2 For the light shaft considered in Exercise 5.1 solve the differential equation of motion by the 'classical' method to obtain expressions for the angular displacement for:
- (a) $0 \leqslant t \leqslant 0.05$,
- (b) $0.05 \leqslant t \leqslant 0.15$,
- (c) $0.15 \leqslant t \leqslant 0.20$, and
- (d) $0.20 \leqslant t$ s.

Answers $\theta_A = -0.2 \cos \omega_n t + 0.2$,
$\theta_B = 0.07665 \sin \omega_n t - 0.13577 \cos \omega_n t + 0.1$,
$\theta_C = -0.17629 \sin \omega_n t - 0.30918 \cos \omega_n t - 0.1$,
$\theta_D = 0.21075 \sin \omega_n t - 0.21531 \cos \omega_n t$ rad,
where $\omega_n = 17.467$ rad/s.

5.3 An undamped spring–mass system has a mass of 500 kg. The period of free vibrations is 0.5 s. The system is initially at rest when the mass is subjected to a force whose variation with time can be approximated to the step function shown in Figure 5.14.

From a phase-plane plot, determine the amplitude of residual vibrations.

Answer   4.3 mm.

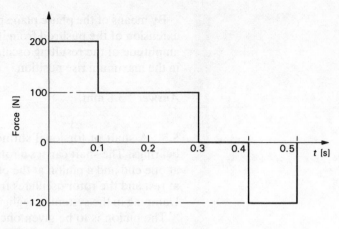

Figure 5.14 Diagram for Problem 5.3.

5.4 A machine element E is controlled by a cam C and a light pushrod AB, as shown diagrammatically in Figure 5.15(a). The cam is designed so that $\ddot{y}$, the acceleration of end A of the pushrod, is as shown in Figure 5.15(b). The mass of the machine element is 50 kg and the stiffness of the pushrod is 100 kN/m.

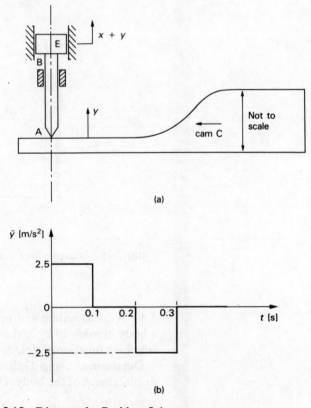

Figure 5.15 Diagram for Problem 5.4.

By means of the phase plane plot of $\dot{x}/\omega_n$ against x, where x is the extension of the pushrod from its unstrained length, determine the amplitude of the resulting oscillation in the pushrod when end A is in the maximum rise position.

Answer 3.8 mm.

5.5 A shaft of torsional stiffness 1750 kN m/rad is supported in bearings. The shaft carries a rotor of moment of inertia 1000 kg m² at one end and a pinion at the other end. Initially the pinion is held at rest and the rotor oscillates freely with an amplitude of 0.02 rad. Damping in the system is negligible.

The pinion is to be given one step-and-return displacement in a clockwise sense, as shown in Figure 5.16, commencing at the instant that the rotor is passing through its mean position in either (a) the clockwise sense or (b) the anti-clockwise sense.

For each case, determine the amplitude of free vibrations of the rotor in the motion that follows the above displacement of the pinion. The phase-plane method is recommended.

Answers (a) 0.048 rad. (b) 0.016 rad.

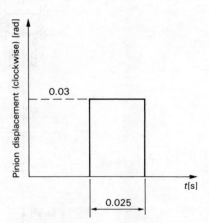

Figure 5.16 Diagram for Problem 5.5.

5.6 A linear system with one degree of freedom is characterized by a body of mass 10 kg and a spring of stiffness 250 N/m. A force F, which is a function of time as shown in Figure 5.17, acts on the body.

Determine, using Duhamel's method, an expression for the displacement of the body. Damping in the system is negligible.

Answer $x(t) = 0.02 + 0.008\ [\sin\ \{5(t - 0.5)\} - \sin 5t]$ m.

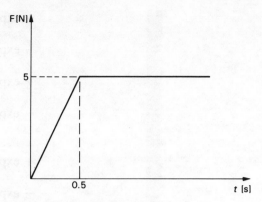

Figure 5.17 Diagram for Problem 5.6.

5.7 Determine the undamped response (displacement) $x(t)$ of a mass-spring system with a single degree of freedom to the force described by the forcing function $f(t) = K_1 \exp(-f_n t)$, where K_1 is a constant and f_n is the natural frequency of the mass–spring system. k is the spring stiffness. Use Duhamel's method.

Answer $x(t) = [4\pi^2 K_1/\{k(4\pi^2 + 1)\}] \{\exp(-f_n t) - \cos(2\pi f_n t)$
$+ (\tfrac{1}{2}/\pi) \sin(2\pi f_n t)\}.$

5.8 Solve the problem presented in Problem 5.7 using the method of Laplace transforms. Use partial fractions to obtain the inverse transform.
   (a)   Obtain the subsidiary equation.
   (b)   Determine the displacement of the system from its equilibrium position at 3 s from the application of the force when $K_1 = 20$ N, $f_n = 0.25$ Hz and $k = 100$ N/m.

Answers   (a) $F(s) = \{4\pi^2 K_1 f_n^2\}/\{k(s + f_n)(s^2 + 4\pi^2 f_n^2)\}$
         (b) 61 mm.

5.9 Determine the undamped responses of a system with a single degree of freedom characterized by a body of mass m and a spring of stiffness k for the time $(n - 1) \le t \le n$ seconds and $n \le t \le (n + 1)$ seconds when a series of force impulses described by the forcing function $f(t)$, shown in Figure 5.18, is applied to the body.
   Use Duhamel's method.

Answer $(n - 1) \le t \le n$:
$\quad x(t) = [(K_1 T^2)/\{m(1 + kT^2/m)\}][\exp(-t/T)$
$\quad\quad - \exp(0/T)\{\cos(k/m)^{0.5}t$
$\quad\quad\quad\quad\quad - \{(m/k)^{0.5}/T\} \sin(k/m)^{0.5}t\}$

$$+ \exp(-1/T)\{\cos(k/m)^{0.5}(t-1)$$
$$- \{(m/k)^{0.5}/T\} \sin(k/m)^{0.5}(t-1)\}$$
$$- \exp(-2/T)\{\cos(k/m)^{0.5}(t-2)$$
$$- \{(m/k)^{0.5}/T\} \sin(k/m)^{0.5}(t-2)\}$$
$$+ \exp(-3/T)\{\cos(k/m)^{0.5}(t-3)$$
$$- \{(m/k)^{0.5}/T\} \sin(k/m)^{0.5}(t-3)\}$$
$$- \exp(-4/T)\{\cos(k/m)^{0.5}(t-4)$$
$$- \{(m/k)^{0.5}/T\} \sin(k/m)^{0.5}(t-4)\}$$
$$+ \cdots$$
$$+ \exp\{-(n-2)/T\}\{\cos(k/m)^{0.5}(t-n+2)$$
$$- \{(m/k)^{0.5}/T\} \sin(k/m)^{0.5}(t-n+2)\}$$
$$- \exp\{-(n-1)/T\}\{\cos(k/m)^{0.5}(t-n+1)$$
$$- \{(m/k)^{0.5}/T\} \sin(k/m)^{0.5}(t-n+1)\}]$$

$n \leq t \leq (n+1)$:
$$x(t) = [(K_1 T^2)/\{m(1 + kT^2/m)\}]$$
$$[- \exp(-0/T)\{\cos(k/m)^{0.5}t$$
$$- \{(m/k)^{0.5}/T\} \sin(k/m)^{0.5}t\}$$
$$+ \exp(-1/T)\{\cos(k/m)^{0.5}(t-1)$$
$$- \{(m/k)^{0.5}/T\} \sin(k/m)^{0.5}(t-1)\}$$
$$- \exp(-2/T)\{\cos(k/m)^{0.5}(t-2)$$
$$- \{(m/k)^{0.5}/T\} \sin(k/m)^{0.5}(t-2)\}$$
$$+ \exp(-3/T)\{\cos(k/m)^{0.5}(t-3)$$
$$- \{(m/k)^{0.5}/T\} \sin(k/m)^{0.5}(t-3)\}$$
$$+ \cdots$$
$$- \exp\{-(n-1)/T\}\{\cos(k/m)^{0.5}(t-n+1)$$
$$- \{(m/k)^{0.5}/T\} \sin(k/m)^{0.5}(t-n+1)\}$$
$$+ \exp(-n/T)\{\cos(k/m)^{0.5}(t-n)$$
$$- \{(m/k)^{0.5}/T\} \sin(k/m)^{0.5}(t-n)\}],$$

where n is an odd natural number.

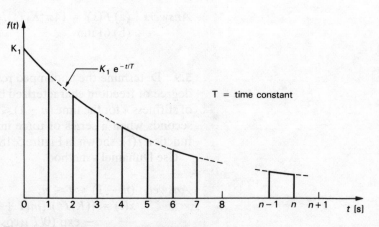

Figure 5.18 Diagram for Problem 5.9.

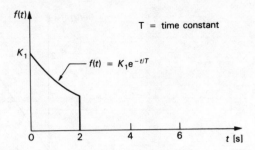

Figure 5.19 Diagram for Problem 5.10.

5.10 An undamped spring–mass system with a single degree of freedom with a body of mass 20 kg and a spring of stiffness 1 kN/m is initially at rest. The body is subjected to a force impulse whose shape is shown in Figure 5.19.

Determine the amplitude of the displacement of the residual vibrations (i.e., for $t > 2$ s) when $K_1 = 1$ N and $T = 5$ s.

In this problem the results from Problem 5.9 will be found useful.

Answer 1.2 mm.

5.11 A mass–spring system with a single degree of freedom has a body of mass m and a natural circular frequency of ω_n.

Determine expressions for the response (displacement) to a force impulse which changes in time as shown in Figure 5.20 for $0 \leq t \leq (2\pi/\omega)$ and $t \geq (2\pi/\omega)$. Damping is negligible.

Answer $x(t) = K_1(\omega \sin \omega_n t - \omega_n \sin \omega t)/\{m\omega_n(\omega^2 - \omega_n^2)\}$
for $0 \leq t \leq (2\pi/\omega)$ and
$x(t) = K_1\omega[\sin (\omega_n t) - \sin \{\omega_n(t - 2\pi/\omega)\}]/$
$\{m\omega_n(\omega^2 - \omega_n^2)\}$ for $t \geq (2\pi/\omega)$.

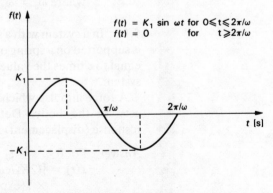

Figure 5.20 Diagram for Problem 5.11.

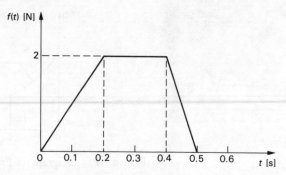

Figure 5.21   Diagram for Problem 5.12.

5.12   A mass–spring system with a single degree of freedom has a body of mass 1 kg and a circular undamped natural frequency of 10 rad/s. The body is subjected to a force impulse $f(t)$ which is shown in Figure 5.21. Damping is negligible.

Determine:
  (a)   the response (displacement) for $t \geqslant 0.5$ s, and
  (b)   the numerical value of the displacement 0.5 s after the application of the impulse.

Answers   (a) $x(t) = -0.01 \sin 10t + 0.01 \sin 10(t - 0.2)$
$+0.02 \sin 10(t - 0.4) - 0.02 \sin 10(t - 0.5)$ m
  (b) 27.8 mm.

5.13   A rectilinear system with a single degree of freedom comprises a body supported by a spring. The undamped circular natural frequency is ω_n. The system includes a viscous damper so that the damping ratio of the system is ξ. A force impulse J is applied to the body at $t = 0$. Given that x is the response (displacement) in the sense of the applied impulse, determine an expression for the displacement $x(t)$.

Answer $x(t) = (J/m\omega_d) \exp(-\xi\omega_n t) \sin \omega_d t$,
    where $\omega_d = \omega_n(1 - \xi^2)^{0.5}$.

5.14   In a system with a single degree of freedom a body of mass m is supported on a spring of stiffness k. A damping force, with a value equal to c times the value of the velocity of the body, appears in the system.

A force impulse which varies with time, as shown in Figure 5.22, acts on the body. Determine, using Duhamel's method, the response (displacement) $x(t)$ to this impulse.

Answer   For $0 \leqslant t \leqslant t_0$
$x(t) = [(2K_1/c\omega_d)/\{1 + (2m/c)^2\omega_d^2\}]$
    $\times [\{\exp(-ct/2m)\{-\sin \omega_d t$
    $- (2m\omega_d/c) \cos \omega_d t\} + (2m/c)\omega_d]$

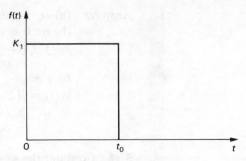

Figure 5.22 Diagram for Problem 5.14.

and for $t \geq t_0$
$$x(t) = [(2K_1/c\omega_d)/\{1 + (2m/c)^2\omega_d^2\}]$$
$$\times [\exp (ct_0/2m) \sin \omega_d(t - t_0)$$
$$- \sin \omega_d t + (2m\omega_d/c) \exp (ct_0/$$
$$2m) \cos \omega_d(t - t_0)$$
$$- (2m\omega_d/c) \cos \omega_d t] \exp (-ct/2m),$$
where $\omega_d = (k/m - c^2/4m^2)^{0.5}$.

5.15 In a seismometer for recording earthquakes a rigid horizontal lever of length L has a small body of mass m at one end and at its other end is attached by a pivot O to the case of the instrument, as shown in Figure 5.23. An elastic vertical spring of stiffness k is pinned to the lever at a distance d from the pivot. A light pointer attached to the small body has a length p.

Determine:

(a) the natural circular frequency of small vibrations of the system, and

(b) the displacement y_P, as a function of time, indicated by the pointer of the seismometer during and after a base displacement described by the function of time shown in Figure 5.24.

Damping of the seismometer can be neglected. The mass of the spring as well as the mass of the lever is negligible in comparison with the body of mass m.

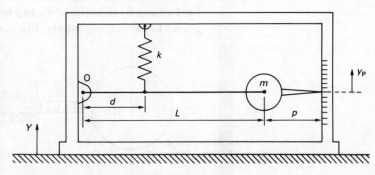

Figure 5.23 Diagram for Problem 5.15.

Answers (a) $\omega_n = (d/L)(k/m)^{0.5}$

(b) for $0 \leqslant t \leqslant t_0$

$y_P(t) = [(L + p)K_2/\{L(1 + \omega_n^2 T^2)\}]\{\exp(-t/T)$
$\quad - \cos \omega_n t + (1/\omega_n T) \sin \omega_n t\}$

for $t \geqslant t_0$

$y_P(t) = [(L + p)K_2/\{L(1 + \omega_n^2 T^2)\}] [\exp(-t_0/T)$
$\quad \times \{\cos \omega_n(t - t_0) - (1/\omega_n T) \sin \omega_n(t - t_0)\}$
$\quad - \cos \omega_n t + (1/\omega_n T) \sin \omega_n t].$

5.16 Consider the seismometer shown in Figure 5.23 in Problem 5.15. Determine the amplitude of the displacement of the residual vibration of the seismometer pointer when the duration of the base displacement, t_0, as shown in Figure 5.24, is 3 s, $K_2 = 10^{-4}$ m and $T = 0.001$ s.

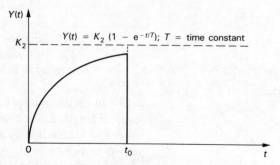

Figure 5.24 Diagram for Problem 5.16.

Assume also that $m = 0.5$ kg, $k = 300$ N/m, $L = 200$ mm, $d = 50$ mm and $p = 30$ mm.

Answer 18.8 mm.

5.17 See Figure 5.25. A circular disc cam C with a geometric centre G can rotate about a fixed axis through O, where OG equals b. It drives a flat-faced follower F and contact between the cam and follower is maintained at all times by the spring S_1.

The follower is connected to a body B of mass M by means of the light spring S_2 of stiffness k, and both F and B are constrained by guides to move horizontally. Friction is everywhere negligible.

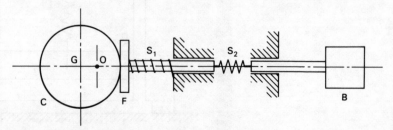

Figure 5.25 Diagram for Problems 5.17 and 5.18.

Initially the system is at rest with the follower F at the extreme left-hand position of its travel. The cam then makes one complete turn at a constant angular velocity ω and stops.

(a)   Show that during the motion of the cam the expression for the displacement of the follower from its initial position is given by

$$b(1 - \cos \omega t).$$

(b)   Determine an expression for the displacement for the residual motion of body B, using Duhamel's method.

(c)   Hence determine the amplitude of the displacement for the residual motion of body B, when $\omega = 8(k/M)^{0.5}$.

Answers   (b) $\{b\omega^2/(\omega^2 - \omega_n^2)\}[\{\cos (2\pi\omega_n/\omega) - 1\} \cos \omega_n t$
$+ \sin (2\pi\omega_n/\omega) \sin \omega_n t]$, where $\omega_n = (k/M)^{0.5}$.
(c) $0.778b$.

5.18   Repeat Problem 5.17 using the method of Laplace transforms.

Answer   Subsidiary equation is:
$F(s) = [b\{1 - \exp (-sT)\}]/\{s(1 + s^2/\omega_n^2)(1 + s^2/\omega^2)\}$,
where $T = 2\pi/\omega$. Using partial fractions:
$F(s) = [1/s + (s/\omega_n^2)(\omega/\omega_n)^2/(\{1 - (\omega/\omega_n)^2\}(1 + s^2/\omega_n^2))$
$- (s/\omega^2)/(\{1 - (\omega/\omega_n)^2\}$
$\times (1 + s^2/\omega^2))]b\{1 - \exp (-sT)\}.$

6

Vibrations of systems with two degrees of freedom

The term degree of freedom has been explained in Chapter 1. A system with two degrees of freedom is characterized by two natural frequencies and two modes of vibration corresponding to the natural frequencies. Figure 6.1 represents a rectilinear two degrees of freedom system without damping.

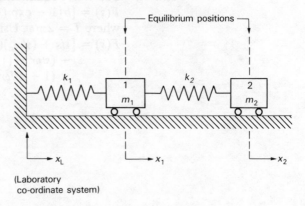

Figure 6.1   System with two degrees of freedom.

Let the body 1 of mass m_1 be given a displacement to the right of x_1; then body 2 has a displacement of x_2 to the right. We assume that $x_1 > x_2$. The free-body diagrams are shown in Figure 6.2.

Newton's second law, applied to the two bodies, gives the following equations:

$$- k_2(x_1 - x_2) - k_1 x_1 = m_1 \ddot{x}_1, \qquad [6.1]$$
$$k_2(x_1 - x_2) = m_2 \ddot{x}_2. \qquad [6.2]$$

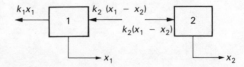

Figure 6.2   Free-body diagrams for system with two degrees of freedom.

We expect that the solutions for x_1 and x_2 will be sinusoidal or cosinusoidal functions of time; thus we postulate:

$$x_1 = X_1 \cos \omega t \quad \text{and} \quad x_2 = X_2 \cos \omega t,$$

where ω is the circular frequency of the resulting vibrations. Substitution of these expressions for x_1 and x_2 in equations [6.1] and [6.2] gives:

$$- k_2(X_1 - X_2) - k_1 X_1 = -m_1 \omega^2 X_1, \qquad [6.3]$$
$$k_2(X_1 - X_2) = -m_2 \omega^2 X_2. \qquad [6.4]$$

Hence, from equation [6.4],

$$X_2 = \{k_2/(k_2 - m_2 \omega^2)\} X_1. \qquad [6.5]$$

Substitution of this expression for X_2 in equation [6.3] gives:

$$k_2^2/(k_2 - m_2 \omega^2) = k_2 + k_1 - m_1 \omega^2$$

or

$$m_1 m_2 \omega^4 - \{m_2(k_1 + k_2) + k_2 m_1\} \omega^2 + k_1 k_2 = 0. \qquad [6.6]$$

The postulated solution x_1, x_2 fulfils the system of equations [6.1] and [6.2] if ω is the solution of the algebraic equation [6.6]. The above quadratic equation in ω^2 is called the frequency equation and gives rise to the following two values of ω^2, namely, ω_1^2 and ω_2^2:

$$\omega_1^2 = \frac{m_2(k_1 + k_2) + k_2 m_1 + [\{m_2(k_1 + k_2) + k_2 m_1\}^2 - 4m_1 m_2 k_1 k_2]^{0.5}}{2m_1 m_2},$$

$$\omega_2^2 = \frac{m_2(k_1 + k_2) + k_2 m_1 - [\{m_2(k_1 + k_2) + k_2 m_1\}^2 - 4m_1 m_2 k_1 k_2]^{0.5}}{2m_1 m_2}.$$

Example 6.1
Natural frequencies and modes of vibration

In Figure 6.1 the symbols have the following values:

$$m_1 = 2 \text{ kg},$$
$$m_2 = 3 \text{ kg},$$
$$k_1 = 2000 \text{ N/m},$$
$$k_2 = 4000 \text{ N/m}.$$

Determine the natural frequencies and the modes of vibration at these natural frequencies.

Given that body 1 is held and body 2 is displaced 10 mm to the right, derive expressions for the ensuing motion after both bodies are released simultaneously.

Solution Substituting numerical values for m_1, m_2, k_1 and k_2 into the frequency equation [6.6], we obtain:

$$2 \times 3\omega^4 - \{3(2000 + 4000) + 4000 \times 2\}\omega^2 + 2000 \times 4000 = 0$$

or

$$6\omega^4 - 26 \times 10^3\omega^2 + 8 \times 10^6 = 0.$$
$$\omega_{1,2}^2 = [26 \times 10^3 \mp \{(26 \times 10^3)^2 - 4 \times 6 \times 8 \times 10^6\}^{0.5}]/12$$
$$= \{26 \times 10^3 \mp 22 \times 10^3\}/12.$$

Thus

$$\omega_1^2 = 333.33 \quad \text{and} \quad \omega_2^2 = 4000.$$

Hence

$$\omega_1 = 18.26 \text{ rad/s} \quad \text{and} \quad \omega_2 = 63.25 \text{ rad/s}.$$

Answer $f_1 = $ **2.91 Hz** and $f_2 = $ **10.1 Hz.**

To find the mode of vibration corresponding to $f_1 = 2.91$ Hz, let us substitute for ω_1^2 the value of 333.33 in equation [6.5]:

$$X_2/X_1 = 4000/(4000 - 3 \times 333.33) = 1.3333.$$

Similarly, for mode of vibration corresponding to $f_2 = 10.1$ Hz, we obtain:

$$X_2/X_1 = 4000/(4000 - 3 \times 4000) = -0.5.$$

These modes of vibration are shown schematically in Figure 6.3. It can be seen from Figure 6.3 that in mode 1 the two bodies are moving in the same direction (with body 2 having the greater amplitude). For mode 2 the two bodies are always moving in opposite directions, or in other words the bodies are out of phase by 180°. In the case of the mode of vibration at 10.1 Hz there is a node, a point of no displacement, between bodies 1 and 2.

Next we have to find expressions for the motion when initially body 2 is displaced and body 1 is held. The general expressions for the ensuing displacements x_1 and x_2 for bodies 1 and 2 respectively are:

$$x_1 = A_1 \sin \omega_1 t + B_1 \cos \omega_1 t + C_1 \sin \omega_2 t + D_1 \cos \omega_2 t,$$
$$x_2 = A_2 \sin \omega_1 t + B_2 \cos \omega_1 t + C_2 \sin \omega_2 t + D_2 \cos \omega_2 t.$$

From the modal shapes we obtain:

$$A_2 = 1.333A_1 \quad \text{and} \quad B_2 = 1.333B_1,$$
$$C_2 = -0.5C_1 \quad \text{and} \quad D_2 = -0.5D_1.$$

Hence,

$$x_2 = 1.333A_1 \sin \omega_1 t + 1.333B_1 \cos \omega_1 t - 0.5C_1 \sin \omega_2 t$$
$$- 0.5D_1 \cos \omega_2 t.$$

When $t = 0$, $x_1 = 0$ and $x_2 = 10$ mm. Therefore,

$$0 = B_1 + D_1 \quad \text{and} \quad 10 = 1.333B_1 - 0.5D_1.$$

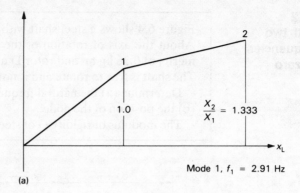

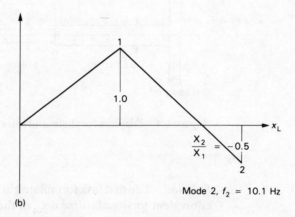

Figure 6.3 Modal shapes of vibration: (a) mode 1: $f_1 = 2.91$ Hz; (b) mode 2: $f_2 = 10.1$ Hz.

Solving the two above equations leads to

$$B_1 = 5.456 \quad \text{and} \quad D_1 = -5.456.$$

Additionally,

$$B_2 = 7.273 \quad \text{and} \quad D_2 = 2.728.$$

When $t = 0$, $\dot{x}_1 = \dot{x}_2 = 0$. Therefore,

$$0 = \omega_1 A_1 + \omega_2 C_1 \quad \text{and} \quad 0 = \omega_1 \times 1.333 A_1 - \omega_2 \times 0.5 C_1.$$

Hence

$$A_1 = C_1 = 0 \quad \text{and also} \quad A_2 = C_2 = 0.$$

The required expressions for displacements of both bodies are:

$$x_1 = (5.46 \cos 18.26t - 5.46 \cos 63.25t) \text{ mm},$$
$$x_2 = (7.27 \cos 18.26t + 2.73 \cos 63.25t) \text{ mm}.$$

**Example 6.2
System with two
natural frequencies,
one being zero**

Figure 6.4 shows a steel shaft with two rotors A and D at its ends. About the axis of rotation of the shaft rotor A has a moment of inertia of 0.36 kg m^2 and rotor D a moment of inertia of 0.6 kg m^2. The shaft is free to rotate and is not fixed in any way.

Determine (a) the natural frequency of torsional oscillations and (b) the position of the node.

The modulus of rigidity G of steel is 85×10^9 N/m^2.

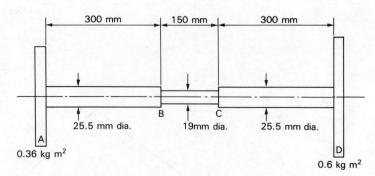

Figure 6.4   Diagram for shafts and rotors. Example 6.2.

Solution   The first task formulated in part (a) of the question is to find the equivalent torsional stiffness s_{eq} of the composite shaft. Each element of the shaft has a torsional stiffness given by:

$$s = GI_P/l.$$

Thus stiffnesses for each element in turn are:

$$s_{AB} = s_{CD} = \{85 \times 10^9 \times \pi(25.5 \times 10^{-3})^4/32\}/0.30$$
$$= 11\,761.4 \text{ N m},$$
$$s_{BC} = \{85 \times 10^9 \times \pi(19.0 \times 10^{-3})^4/32\}/0.15$$
$$= 7250.1 \text{ N m}.$$

Stiffnesses in series act like electrical resistances in parallel, thus the equivalent stiffness of the system of shafts, s_{eq}, is given by:

$$1/s_{eq} = 1/s_{AB} + 1/s_{BC} + 1/s_{CD}$$
$$= 2/11\,761.4 + 1/7250.1$$

or

$$s_{eq} = 3247.1 \text{ N m}.$$

The two rotors at A and D may now be regarded as being connected by a shaft of torsional stiffness of 3247.1 N m, as shown in Figure 6.5. Let rotor A have an angular displacement of θ_A and rotor D an angular displacement θ_D. The torques acting on the rotors and the angular accelerations of the rotors are also shown in Figure 6.6.

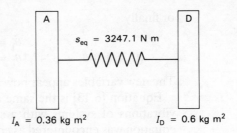

Figure 6.5 Equivalent system for shafts and rotors in Example 6.2.

Considering moments about the shaft axis (through A and D) for the two rotors we obtain the equations of motion:

$$-3247.1(\theta_A - \theta_D) = 0.36\ddot{\theta}_A, \qquad [6.7]$$
$$3247.1(\theta_A - \theta_D) = 0.6\ddot{\theta}_D. \qquad [6.8]$$

After adding equations [6.7] and [6.8] we obtain instead of system [6.7–6.8]:

$$0.6\ddot{\theta}_A + \ddot{\theta}_D = 0, \qquad [6.9]$$
$$0.36\ddot{\theta}_A + 3247.1(\theta_A - \theta_D) = 0. \qquad [6.10]$$

Let us define new variables:

$$\theta_1 = 0.6\theta_A + \theta_D,$$
$$\theta_2 = \theta_A - \theta_D.$$

Therefore,

$$\theta_A = (\theta_1 + \theta_2)/1.6,$$
$$\theta_D = (\theta_1 - 0.6\theta_2)/1.6. \qquad [6.11]$$

The set of equations [6.9] and [6.10] is transformed to:

$$\ddot{\theta}_1 = 0,$$
$$(0.36/1.6)(\ddot{\theta}_1 + \ddot{\theta}_2) + 3247.1\theta_2 = 0$$

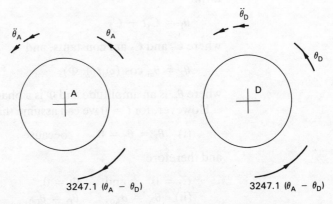

Figure 6.6 Torques and angular accelerations acting on rotors A and D (Example 6.2).

or finally:

$$\ddot{\theta}_1 = 0, \tag{6.12}$$
$$(0.36/1.6)\ddot{\theta}_2 + 3247.1\theta_2 = 0. \tag{6.13}$$

The new variables appear now separately in both equations.

Equation [6.13] is the same as the standard form for free, undamped vibrations of systems with a single degree of freedom. This standard equation was encountered as equation [1.3] in Chapter 1.

We can assume solutions of the form:

$$\theta_A = X_A \cos(\omega_n t) \qquad \text{and} \qquad \theta_D = X_D \cos(\omega_n t)$$

or

$$\theta_1 = X_1 \cos(\omega_n t) \qquad \text{where} \qquad X_1 = 0.6X_A + X_D,$$

and

$$\theta_2 = X_2 \cos(\omega_n t) \qquad \text{where} \qquad X_2 = X_A - X_D. \tag{6.14}$$

Inserting equation [6.14] into [6.13] we obtain an equation in ω_n^2 for the undamped circular natural frequency of torsional oscillations. Hence the undamped circular natural frequency ω_n is given by:

$$\omega_n^2 = 3247.1 \times 1.6/0.36$$

or

$$\omega_n = 120.13 \text{ rad/s} \qquad (f_n = 19.12 \text{ Hz}).$$

Answer to part (a) $\omega_n = \textbf{120.13 rad/s}$ or $f_n = \textbf{19.12 Hz.}$

Before we consider part (b) of the question, we will look at a more complete analysis which confirms the above and gives a better understanding of the problem. This approach will give the complete (general) solution of the system of equations [6.12–6.13].

Let us consider again equations [6.12] and [6.13]. From these equations we can deduce that the general solution of the system of equations is in the form:

$$\theta_1 = C_1 t + C_2,$$

where C_1 and C_2 are constants, and

$$\theta_2 = \theta_m \cos(\omega_n t + \Phi),$$

where θ_m is an amplitude and Φ is a phase angle.

However, for $t = 0$ we can assume that:

(i) $\dot{\theta}_1 = \dot{\theta}_2 = 0,$ because $\dot{\theta}_A = \dot{\theta}_D = 0$

and therefore

$$C_1 = 0 \qquad \text{and} \qquad \Phi = 0.$$
(ii) $\theta_A = \theta_{A0}, \qquad \theta_D = \theta_{D0},$

therefore

$$\theta_1 = \theta_{10} = C_2 = 0.6\theta_{A0} + \theta_{D0}$$

and

$$\theta_2 = \theta_{20} = \theta_m = \theta_{A0} - \theta_{D0}.$$

We know that ω_n is 120.13 rad/s; hence for θ_1 and θ_2 we obtain finally:

$$\theta_1 = 0.6\theta_{A0} + \theta_{D0} = C_2,$$
$$\theta_2 = (\theta_{A0} - \theta_{D0}) \cos (120.13t).$$

Taking into account the relations [6.11] one obtains:

$$\theta_A = (0.6\theta_{A0} + \theta_{D0})/1.6 + \{(\theta_{A0} - \theta_{D0})/1.6\} \cos (120.13t),$$
$$\theta_D = (0.6\theta_{A0} + \theta_{D0})/1.6 - \{0.6(\theta_{A0} - \theta_{D0})/1.6\} \cos (120.13t).$$

θ_A and θ_D describe torsional oscillations relative to a new equilibrium position,

$$\theta_{eq} = (0.6_{A0} + \theta_{D0})/1.6,$$

which is determined by the initial conditions.

We can now define a new polar co-ordinate appropriate to describing torsional oscillations around the equilibrium position:

$$\theta' = \theta - (0.6\theta_{A0} + \theta_{D0})/1.6. \tag{6.15}$$

Hence

$$\theta'_A = \theta_A - (0.6\theta_{A0} + \theta_{D0})/1.6$$

and

$$\theta'_D = \theta_D - (0.6\theta_{A0} + \theta_{D0})/1.6.$$

Therefore,

$$\theta'_A = \{(\theta_{A0} - \theta_{D0})/1.6\} \cos (120.13t),$$
$$\theta'_D = -\{0.6(\theta_{A0} - \theta_{D0})/1.6\} \cos (120.13t). \tag{6.16}$$

If the initial torsional displacements of the rotors, θ_{A0} and θ_{D0} (in the fixed laboratory system), are expressed in the new polar co-ordinate system connected with the new equilibrium position, then:

$$\theta'_{A0} = (\theta_{A0} - \theta_{D0})/1.6,$$
$$\theta'_{D0} = -0.6(\theta_{A0} - \theta_{D0})/1.6. \tag{6.17}$$

Hence

$$\theta'_A = \theta'_{A0} \cos (120.13t),$$
$$\theta'_D = -0.6\theta'_{A0} \cos (120.13t). \tag{6.18}$$

From equations [6.18] one may deduce additionally that:

$$\theta'_D/\theta'_A = \theta'_{D0}/\theta'_{A0} = -0.6. \tag{6.19}$$

The torsional oscillations of both rotors are described only by one natural frequency, even though there are two rotors characterized by different values of mass and moment of inertia, and the system appears to have two degrees of freedom. There are in fact two natural frequencies, but the lowest one is zero (see equation [6.12]).

It should be noted that the problem of determining the natural frequency of torsional oscillations could also have been solved by an identical method to that used in Example 6.1.

Solution of (b)   Next we have to find the position of the node. Let us denote, for simplicity, θ_A' as θ_A, θ_B' as θ_B, θ_C' as θ_C, etc. θ_A is the angular displacement of the rotor A and θ_D is the angular displacement of the rotor D.

Figure 6.7(a) shows the middle section BC of the shaft (see also Figure 6.4), where we assume the node N appears. The straight line $P_{B0}P_{C0}$ (parallel to the cylinder (shaft) axis BC) lies on the surface of revolution of the cylinder $\mathscr{P}_0$. The curve P_BP_C, located on the surface of the cylinder $\mathscr{P}_0$, forms a straight line when the surface of the cylinder is unfolded into a plane. The plane $\mathscr{P}_1$ through $P_{B0}P_{C0}$ and the shaft axis is fixed in space and it defines the equilibrium position of the torsionally oscillating shaft. Let us consider points lying on the straight line $P_{B0}P_{C0}$ when the shaft is in equilibrium. At a certain instant of time during the torsional oscillation these points are located on the curve P_BP_C.

Let us develop the surface $\mathscr{P}_0$ in the plane of Figure 6.7(b) (see Figures 6.7(a) and 6.7(b)), and let us define a co-ordinate system xy on plane $\mathscr{P}_0$ (Figure 6.7(b)). Let x_n be a distance along the x axis between the node N and the origin of the co-ordinate system xy.

We may write (see Figure 6.7):

$$\theta_B R/(L_{BC}/2 + x_n) = -\theta_C R/(L_{BC}/2 - x_n).$$

Therefore we have:

$$\theta_B/(75 + x_n) = -\theta_C/(75 - x_n). \qquad [6.20]$$

We know that the value of the torque throughout the shaft is the same, hence:

$$s_{eq}(\theta_D - \theta_A) = s_{AB}(\theta_B - \theta_A)$$

or

$$3247.1(\theta_D/\theta_A - 1) = 11761.4(\theta_B/\theta_A - 1). \qquad [6.21]$$

Additionally,

$$s_{AB}(\theta_B - \theta_A) = s_{BC}(\theta_C - \theta_B)$$

or

$$11761.4(1 - \theta_A/\theta_B) = 7250.1(\theta_C/\theta_B - 1). \qquad [6.22]$$

Finally we have

$$\theta_D/\theta_A = -0.6. \qquad [6.23]$$

Equations [6.20–6.23] enable us to determine the value of x_n, i.e., to

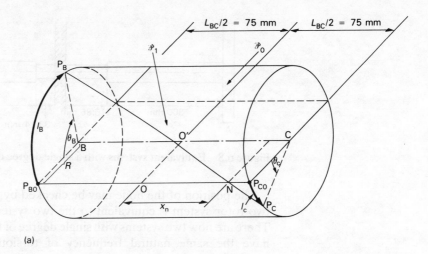

(a)

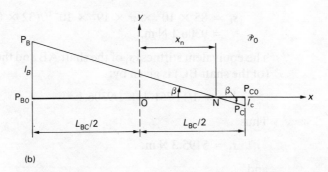

(b)

Figure 6.7   Example 6.2 (a) Diagram showing position of the node in the central section of shaft; (b)Diagram for calculating position of node from shaft centre.

find the position of the node N. From equation [6.21] and equation [6.23] we obtain:

$$(\theta_B/\theta_A) = 0.55827.$$

Additionally, from equation [6.22] we have

$$(\theta_C/\theta_B) = -0.28359.$$

Finally equation [6.20] leads to:

$$-(75 - x_n)/(75 + x_n) = -0.28359$$

or

$$x_n = 41.859 \text{ mm}.$$

Answer to part (b)   The node is approximately **42 mm** from the centre of the shaft or **417 mm** from the rotor A.

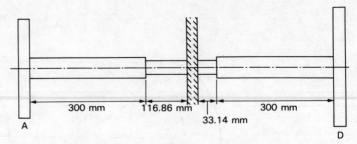

Figure 6.8   Equivalent systems with a single degree of freedom.

The position of the node may be checked by a different method. The two rotor system is equivalent to the two systems shown in Figure 6.8. There are now two systems with single degree of freedom and both should have the same natural frequency of torsional oscillations, namely 19.12 Hz.

Let us consider the left-hand system first (Figure 6.8). The stiffness of the 116.86 mm long shaft is given by the equation:

$$s_L = 85 \times 10^9 \times \pi \times 19^4 \times 10^{-12}/(32 \times 0.11686)$$
$$= 9306.1 \text{ N m.}$$

The equivalent stiffness s_1 of the shaft AB and the 116.86 mm long section (of the shaft BC) is given by:

$$1/s_1 = 1/11\,761.4 + 1/9306.1.$$

Thus

$$s_1 = 5195.3 \text{ N m,}$$

and

$$\omega_n^2 = 5195.3/0.36 \quad \text{and} \quad \omega_n = 120.13 \text{ rad/s.}$$

Hence

$$f_n = 19.12 \text{ Hz.}$$

In the right-hand system the 33.14 mm long shaft has a stiffness given by the equation:

$$s_R = 85 \times 10^9 \times \pi \times 19^4 \times 10^{-12}/(32 \times 0.03314)$$
$$= 32\,815.6 \text{ N m.}$$

The equivalent stiffness s_2 of the combined shaft of the right-hand system is given by:

$$1/s_2 = 1/11\,761.4 + 1/32\,815.6.$$

Thus

$$s_2 = 8658.2 \text{ N m.}$$

And

$$\omega_n^2 = 8658.2/0.6.$$

Hence

$$f_n = 19.12 \, \text{Hz}.$$

The natural frequency of torsional oscillations has been found to have a value of 19.12 Hz for both systems, the same value as previously obtained. Thus the calculated position of the node is confirmed as correct. Of course, this checking of the node position could be the basis for an alternative method for determining the position of the node.

Example 6.3
Natural frequencies and modes for double pendulum

Figure 6.9 shows a double pendulum in which A and B are two point masses and OA and AB are strings of length l. The co-ordinates of the two masses in the x direction are x_1 and x_2, as shown.

Determine for small amplitudes of oscillation:

(a)   the natural frequencies of the system,
(b)   the ratio of the amplitudes of x_1 and x_2 for each natural frequency, and
(c)   the positions of the nodes for the two modes of vibration.

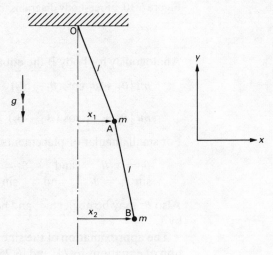

Figure 6.9   Example 6.3. Double pendulum.

Solution   (a)   The free-body diagrams for the two point masses are shown in Figure 6.10, where we note that two new co-ordinates θ_1 and θ_2 have been introduced.

The motion of body A in the tangential and normal directions, respectively, is described in the laboratory system (the co-ordinate system origin at O) by the following equations:

$$ml\ddot{\theta}_1 = -mg \sin \theta_1 - T_2 \sin (\theta_1 - \theta_2),$$
$$ml\dot{\theta}_1^2 = -mg \cos \theta_1 - T_2 \cos (\theta_1 - \theta_2) + T_1. \qquad [6.24]$$

Figure 6.10   Free-body diagrams for bodies A and B of double pendulum.

Analogously for body B the equations of motion are:

$$ml\{\ddot{\theta}_2 + \ddot{\theta}_1 \cos (\theta_1 - \theta_2) - \dot{\theta}_1^2 \sin (\theta_1 - \theta_2)\} = -mg \sin \theta_2,$$
$$[6.25]$$
$$ml\{\dot{\theta}_2^2 + \dot{\theta}_1^2 \cos (\theta_1 - \theta_2) + \ddot{\theta}_1 \sin (\theta_1 - \theta_2)\} = -mg \cos \theta_2 + T_2.$$

For small angular displacements, we have:

$$\theta_1 = x_1/l \quad \text{and} \quad \theta_2 = (x_2 - x_1)/l,$$
$$\sin \theta_1 = \theta_1 \quad \text{and} \quad \sin \theta_2 = \theta_2.$$

Also θ^2 may be neglected, and hence cosine terms may be approximated by 1.

The approximation of the sine and cosine terms leads to the simplification of equations [6.24] and [6.25]. Namely,

$$ml\ddot{\theta}_1 = -mg\theta_1 - T_2(\theta_1 - \theta_2),$$
$$[6.26]$$
$$ml\dot{\theta}_1^2 = -mg - T_2 + T_1,$$
$$ml\{\ddot{\theta}_2 + \ddot{\theta}_1 - \dot{\theta}_1^2(\theta_1 - \theta_2)\} = -mg\theta_2,$$
$$[6.27]$$
$$ml\{\dot{\theta}_2^2 + \dot{\theta}_1^2 + \ddot{\theta}_1(\theta_1 - \theta_2)\} = -mg + T_2.$$
$$[6.28]$$

From equation [6.28] we have:

$$T_2 = ml\{\dot{\theta}_2^2 + \dot{\theta}_1^2 + \ddot{\theta}_1(\theta_1 - \theta_2)\} + mg.$$

Eliminating T_2 from equation [6.26] we obtain:

$$ml\ddot{\theta}_1 = -mg\theta_1 - ml\{\dot{\theta}_2^2 + \dot{\theta}_1^2 + \ddot{\theta}_1(\theta_1 - \theta_2)\}(\theta_1 - \theta_2)$$
$$- mg(\theta_1 - \theta_2).$$
$$[6.29]$$

Terms involving $\dot{\theta}^2\theta$ and $\ddot{\theta}\theta^2$ may be neglected and hence from equations [6.27] and [6.29] we obtain:

$$ml(\ddot{\theta}_1 + \ddot{\theta}_2) + mg\theta_2 = 0, \qquad [6.30]$$
$$ml\ddot{\theta}_1 + mg\theta_1 + mg(\theta_1 - \theta_2) = 0. \qquad [6.31]$$

Finally, we write both the above equations [6.30] and [6.31] in terms of x_1 and x_2 in the following form:

$$m(\ddot{x}_1 + \ddot{x}_2 - \ddot{x}_1) + mg(x_2 - x_1)/l = 0$$

and

$$m\ddot{x}_1 + mgx_1/l + mg(x_1 - x_2 + x_1)/l = 0,$$

or

$$\ddot{x}_1 = g(x_2 - 3x_1)/l, \qquad [6.32]$$
$$\ddot{x}_2 = g(x_1 - x_2)/l. \qquad [6.33]$$

To find the values of the natural frequencies of the system we assume that the solutions for x_1 and x_2 have the form:

$$x_1 = X_1 \sin \omega t \qquad \text{and} \qquad x_2 = X_2 \sin \omega t.$$

Hence

$$g(X_2 - 3X_1)/l = -\omega^2 X_1. \qquad [6.34]$$

And

$$g(-X_2 + X_1)/l = -\omega^2 X_2. \qquad [6.35]$$

From equation [6.34],

$$X_2/X_1 = 3 - l\omega^2/g \qquad [6.36]$$

Substituting for X_1 in equation [6.35] gives:

$$(g/l)\{-X_2 + X_2/(3 - l\omega^2/g)\} = -\omega^2 X_2.$$

Hence the following frequency equation is obtained:

$$\omega^4 - (4g/l)\omega^2 + 2g^2/l^2 = 0.$$

Therefore,

$$\omega_{1,2}^2 = 2g/l \mp \{4g^2/l^2 - 2g^2/l^2\}^{0.5}$$
$$= 2g/l \mp 2^{0.5}(g/l).$$

Thus

$$\omega_1^2 = 0.5858(g/l) \qquad \text{and} \qquad \omega_2^2 = 3.4142(g/l).$$
$$\omega_1 = 0.7654(g/l)^{0.5} \qquad \text{and} \qquad \omega_2 = 1.8478(g/l)^{0.5}.$$
$$f_1 = 0.122(g/l)^{0.5} \qquad \text{and} \qquad f_2 = 0.294(g/l)^{0.5}.$$

Answer to question (a) The natural frequencies of the system are:
$$f_1 = \mathbf{0.122(g/l)^{0.5}} \text{ and } f_2 = \mathbf{0.294(g/l)^{0.5}}.$$

 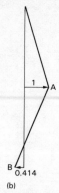

(a) (b)

Figure 6.11 Modal shapes of vibration for double pendulum: (a) mode 1: $f_1 = 0.122(g/l)^{0.5}$; (b) mode 2: $f_2 = 0.294(g/l)^{0.5}$.

(b) The ratio of the amplitudes and modal shapes of vibration. The ratio X_2/X_1 is obtained from equation [6.36]. Thus when $\omega_1^2 = 0.5858g/l$

$$X_2/X_1 = 3 - 0.5858 = 2.4142.$$

And for the second mode of vibration when $\omega_2^2 = 3.4142g/l$

$$X_2/X_1 = 3 - 3.4142 = -0.4142.$$

The modal shapes of vibration are shown in Figure 6.11.

Answer to question (b)   For the first mode of vibration $X_2/X_1 = $ **2.41** and for the second mode of vibration $X_2/X_1 = $ **−0.41.**

(c) In the first mode of vibration there is no node, apart from the point of support. In the second mode of vibration the distance of the node from the support is:

$$l(1 + 1/1.414) = 1.707l.$$

Answer to question (c)   In the second mode of vibration the node is located at a distance **1.707 l** from the support.

**Example 6.4
Motor vehicle as a
system with
translation and
rotation**

A motor vehicle has a mass of 4800 kg and a moment of inertia about a transverse axis passing through the mass centre of 14 000 kg m². The mass centre is 1.24 m in front of the rear axle and 2.6 m behind the front axle. The combined stiffness of the rear springs is 120 kN/m and of the front springs is 82 kN/m.

Working from first principles, show that the frequency equation for small oscillations of the vehicle in a vertical plane through the vehicle mass centre is

$$\omega^4 - 94.9\omega^2 + 2159 = 0,$$

where ω is the circular frequency in rad/s.

Hence determine the distances from the mass centre of the two centres of oscillation corresponding to the two natural frequencies.

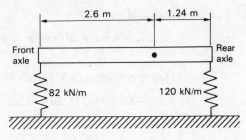

Figure 6.12   Model of motor vehicle with two degrees of freedom (Example 6.4).

Solution   A simple model for the vehicle is a rigid body on two unequal springs, as shown in Figure 6.12.

When the rigid body is displaced in the vertical plane from its static equilibrium, the position of the body at any instant in time may be defined in terms of the co-ordinates y_G and θ, as shown in Figure 6.13. The additional compressions (relative to the equilibrium position shown in Figure 6.13) of both systems of springs, namely the front springs and the rear springs, denoted as y_1 and y_2, respectively, are given by:

$$y_1 = y_G - 2.6\theta \qquad \text{and} \qquad y_2 = y_G + 1.24\theta.$$

Figure 6.13 also shows the accelerations of the body and the values of the forces relative to the equilibrium values. The motion of the body is described by a system of equations based on Newton's second law, namely: $\Sigma F_y = m\ddot{y}_G$ or

$$-82 \times 10^3(y_G - 2.6\theta) - 120 \times 10^3(y_G + 1.24\theta) = 4.8 \times 10^3\ddot{y}_G$$
$$[6.37]$$

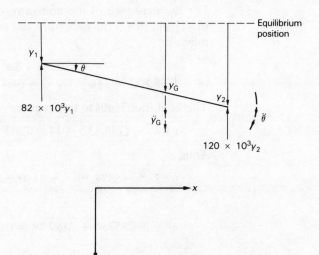

Figure 6.13   Forces and displacements for motor vehicle body.

and $\Sigma M_G = I_G \ddot\theta$ or

$$2.6 \times 82 \times 10^3(y_G - 2.6\theta) - 1.24 \times 120 \times 10^3(y_G + 1.24\theta)$$
$$= 14 \times 10^3 \ddot\theta. \quad [6.38]$$

Hence equation [6.37] leads to:

$$-82y_G + 213.2\theta - 120y_G - 148.8\theta = 4.8\ddot{y}_G$$

or

$$-202y_G + 64.4\theta = 4.8\ddot{y}_G \qquad [6.39]$$

and similarly from the equation [6.38] we obtain:

$$213.2y_G - 554.32\theta - 148.8y_G - 184.512\theta = 14\ddot\theta$$

or

$$64.4y_G - 738.832\theta = 14\ddot\theta. \qquad [6.40]$$

Let us assume the solution of the above differential equations in the form:

$$\theta = X \sin \omega t \qquad \text{and} \qquad y_G = Y \sin \omega t.$$

After substituting θ and y_G into equations [6.39] and [6.40], which describe the motion of the system, we obtain:

$$-202Y + 64.4X = -4.8\omega^2 Y$$

and

$$64.4Y - 738.832X = -14\omega^2 X.$$

The above two equations may be rearranged and written as

$$-64.4X + (202 - 4.8\omega^2)Y = 0, \qquad [6.41]$$
$$(738.832 - 14\omega^2)X \qquad\qquad - 64.4Y = 0. \qquad [6.42]$$

For the existence of the non-zero solution of homogeneous equations [6.41] and [6.42] the necessary and sufficient condition is that the determinant:

$$\begin{vmatrix} -64.4 & 202 - 4.8\omega^2 \\ 738.832 - 14\omega^2 & -64.4 \end{vmatrix} = 0.$$

This condition leads to the frequency equation:

$$64.4^2 - (738.832 - 14\omega^2)(202 - 4.8\omega^2) = 0.$$

Thus

$$67.2\omega^4 - 6374.39\omega^2 + 145096.7 = 0$$

or

$$\omega^4 - 94.857\omega^2 + 2159.18 = 0.$$

Answer The frequency equation with verified, approximate coefficients is $\omega^4 - 94.9\omega^2 + 2159 = 0$.

The natural frequencies are obtained from the frequency equation, hence:

$$\omega_{1,2}^2 = 47.43 \mp (2249.46 - 2159.18)^{0.5}.$$
$$\omega_1^2 = 37.928 \quad \text{and} \quad \omega_2^2 = 56.932.$$

Hence

$$\omega_1 = 6.159 \quad \text{and} \quad \omega_2 = 7.545.$$

Substituting $\omega_1^2 = 37.928$ into equation [6.41] leads to the expression for the first mode of vibration:

$$-64.4X + 19.95Y = 0$$

and therefore, $X/Y = 0.3098$.

Similarly, for the second mode of vibration (for $\omega_2^2 = 56.932$) we have:

$$X/Y = -1.1067.$$

Since

$$y_1 = y_G - 2.6\theta \quad \text{and} \quad y_1 = Y_1 \sin \omega t$$

we may write:

$$Y_1 = Y - 2.6X. \qquad [6.43]$$

Similarly,

$$Y_2 = Y + 1.24X. \qquad [6.44]$$

For the first mode of vibration we have: $X/Y = 0.3098$. From equation [6.43] we obtain:

$$Y_1 = 0.1945Y,$$

and

$$Y_2 = 1.384Y \quad \text{from equation [6.44].}$$

The position of the node (centre of oscillation) for the first mode of vibration is shown in Figure 6.14 and, as may be seen from the diagram, is located at a distance x_1 from the front springs. Thus we have:

$$x_1/0.1945 = 1.24/0.384 \quad \text{and} \quad x_1 = 0.6281 \text{ m.}$$

For the second mode of vibration $X/Y = -1.1067$ and from equations [6.43] and [6.44] one obtains:

$$Y_1 = 3.8774Y \quad \text{and} \quad Y_2 = -0.3723Y.$$

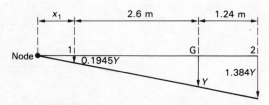

Figure 6.14 Position of node for first mode of vibration.

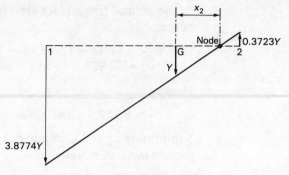

Figure 6.15   Position of node for second mode of vibration.

Figure 6.15 shows the node at a distance x_2 from the centre of mass, G. Thus

$$x_2/Y = 2.6/(2.8774Y) \qquad \text{and hence} \qquad x_2 = 0.9036 \text{ m}.$$

Answer   For the first mode of vibration the node (centre of oscillation) is at a distance of **3.228 m** forward of the centre of mass, and for the second mode of vibration the node is at a distance of **0.904 m** behind the centre of mass (or 0.336 m in front of the rear axle).

Example 6.5
Natural frequencies
for a solid sphere on
a chain

A solid sphere, 0.4 m in diameter, is suspended by a light chain, 0.8 m long. Determine the natural frequencies of small oscillations.

Solution   A free-body diagram for the sphere is shown in Figure 6.16.

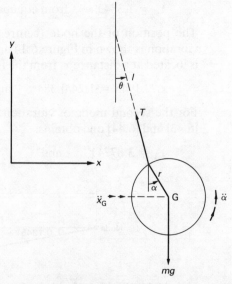

Figure 6.16   Free-body diagram for sphere on a chain (Example 6.5).

When the sphere is displaced the chain is inclined at an angle θ to the vertical, and a line joining the centre of mass G of the sphere to the point of attachment is inclined at α to the vertical. Then x_G, the horizontal displacement of G from its equilibrium position, is given by:

$$x_G = l \sin \theta + r \sin \alpha,$$

where l is the length of the chain and r is the radius of the sphere. Provided that the displacements are small, x_G may be written as:

$$x_G = l\theta + r\alpha.$$

The equations of motion for the sphere are:

$$\Sigma F_x = m\ddot{x}_G \qquad \text{(in the } x \text{ direction)},$$

and

$$\Sigma M_G = I_G \ddot{\alpha}.$$

Thus

$$-T \sin \theta = m(l\ddot{\theta} + r\ddot{\alpha})$$

and

$$Tr \sin (\theta - \alpha) = I_G \ddot{\alpha},$$

where T is the tension in the chain and m the mass of the sphere.

For small oscillations the above two equations may be written as:

$$-T\theta = m(l\ddot{\theta} + r\ddot{\alpha}), \qquad [6.45]$$
$$Tr(\theta - \alpha) = I_G \ddot{\alpha}. \qquad [6.46]$$

We assume that the solution of equations [6.45] and [6.46] is of the form:

$$\theta = A \sin \omega t \qquad \text{and} \qquad \alpha = B \sin \omega t.$$

Therefore

$$-TA = m(-l\omega^2 A - r\omega^2 B), \qquad [6.47]$$
$$Tr(A - B) = -I_G \omega^2 B. \qquad [6.48]$$

Recognizing that $T = mg$ for small displacements ($T = mg \cos \theta$, exactly) we rewrite equation [6.47] as:

$$A = \{r\omega^2/(g - l\omega^2)\}B.$$

Substitution of the expression for A in equation [6.48] gives:

$$mgr[\{r\omega^2/(g - l\omega^2)\} - 1] = -I_G \omega^2$$

or

$$mgr^2\omega^2 - mg^2r + mgrl\omega^2 = -gI_G\omega^2 + lI_G\omega^4$$

or

$$lI_G\omega^4 + (-gI_G - mgrl - mgr^2)\omega^2 + mg^2r = 0.$$

For a sphere, $I_G = 0.4mr^2$; thus

$$0.4lr\omega^4 - (0.4gr + gl + gr)\omega^2 + g^2 = 0.$$

For this particular problem, $r = 0.2$ m and $l = 0.8$ m, and also $g = 9.81$ m/s^2, so

$$0.064\omega^4 - 10.5948\omega^2 + 96.2361 = 0.$$

And

$$\omega^4 - 165.544\omega^2 + 1503.69 = 0.$$

Thus

$$\omega_{1,2}^2 = 82.772 \mp \{6851.20 - 1503.69\}^{0.5}.$$
$$\omega_1^2 = 9.6453 \quad \text{and} \quad \omega_2^2 = 155.899.$$
$$\omega_1 = 3.1057 \text{ rad/s} \quad \text{and} \quad \omega_2 = 12.486 \text{ rad/s}.$$

Answer   The natural frequencies of small oscillations are **0.494 Hz** and **1.99 Hz**.

It is interesting to note that if the sphere and chain were regarded as a simple pendulum of length 1.0 m the natural frequency would be $(0.5/\pi)(9.81)^{0.5}$ or 0.498 Hz. Thus in the case of the first mode of vibration the sphere is oscillating like a simple pendulum.

Example 6.6
Natural frequencies for a bar in bending and torsion

A uniform slender bar, of mass 100 kg, is supported by a tubular shaft as shown in Figure 6.17. The torsional stiffness of the shaft is 8000 N m/rad, and the lateral stiffness is 30 000 N/m. The bar is 0.8 m long and is supported by the shaft at a point very close to its end.

Determine the natural frequencies of small amplitude free vibrations of the bar.

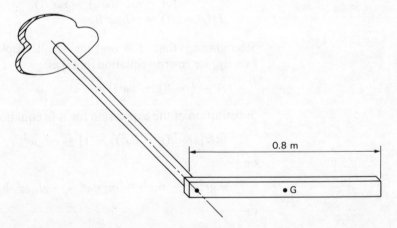

Figure 6.17   Diagram of bar for Example 6.6.

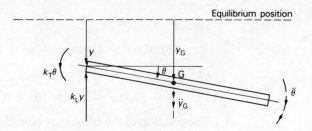

Figure 6.18   Free-body diagram for bar in bending and torsion (Example 6.6).

Solution   The free-body diagram for the bar is shown in Figure 6.18. k_T is the torsional stiffness of the shaft of 8000 N m/rad and k_L is its lateral stiffness of 30 000 N/m.

When the bar is displaced from its equilibrium position the vertical deflection of the point where the shaft is attached is y (Figure 6.18). y_G is the displacement of the centre of mass G of the bar and θ is the angular inclination of the bar. Thus, we may write:

$$y_G = y + 0.4\theta.$$

The equations of motion for the bar are:

$$-k_L(y_G - 0.4\theta) = m\ddot{y}_G,$$
$$-k_T\theta + 0.4k_L(y_G - 0.4\theta) = I_G\ddot{\theta},$$

where m is the mass of the bar and I_G is its moment of inertia about an axis through the centre of mass G. We assume that the solution of the system of equations takes the form:

$$y_G = Y \sin \omega t \quad \text{and} \quad \theta = X \sin \omega t.$$

Hence

$$-k_L(Y - 0.4X) = -m\omega^2 Y,$$
$$-k_T X + 0.4k_L(Y - 0.4X) = -I_G\omega^2 X$$

or

$$0.4k_L X + (m\omega^2 - k_L)Y = 0,$$
$$(k_T + 0.16k_L - I_G\omega^2)X - 0.4k_L Y = 0.$$

For the existence of the non-zero solution of the above system of homogeneous equations the necessary and sufficient condition is that the determinant:

$$\begin{vmatrix} 0.4k_L & -(k_L - m\omega^2) \\ (k_T + 0.4^2k_L - I_G\omega^2) & -0.4k_L \end{vmatrix} = 0.$$

This condition leads to the frequency equation:

$$-0.4^2k_L^2 + (k_T + 0.4^2k_L - I_G\omega^2)(k_L - m\omega^2) = 0$$

or

$$mI_G\omega^4 - (I_G k_L + mk_T + 0.4^2 mk_L)\omega^2 + k_L k_T = 0.$$

$$I_G = 100 \times 0.8^2/12 = 5.33333 \text{ kg m}^2.$$

Hence

$$533.333\omega^4 - 1.440 \times 10^6\omega^2 + 240 \times 10^6 = 0$$

or

$$\omega^4 - 2700\omega^2 + 450 \times 10^3 = 0.$$

The solution of the frequency equation is:

$$\omega_{1,2}^2 = 1350 \mp \{1350^2 - 450 \times 10^3\}^{0.5}.$$
$$\omega_1^2 = 178.46 \quad \text{and} \quad \omega_2^2 = 2521.54.$$
$$\omega_1 = 13.36 \text{ rad/s} \quad \text{and} \quad \omega_2 = 50.21 \text{ rad/s}.$$

Answer The natural frequencies of free vibrations are **2.13 Hz** and **7.99 Hz**.

6.1 Undamped forced vibrations

Let us consider a force $F_1 \cos \omega_F t$ applied to body 1 (Figure 6.1) and acting towards the right. The equation of motion for body 1 becomes:

$$F_1 \cos \omega_F t - k_2(x_1 - x_2) - k_1 x_1 = m_1 \ddot{x}_1. \tag{6.49}$$

The equation of motion for body 2 (equation [6.2]) remains the same. The responses, x_1 and x_2, have amplitudes X_{1F} and X_{2F}, respectively, and may be assumed to be in the form:

$$x_1 = X_{1F} \cos \omega_F t \quad \text{and} \quad x_2 = X_{2F} \cos \omega_F t.$$

The subscript F is used to indicate that we are now dealing with a forced vibration problem and the considered system may vibrate at any applied circular frequency ω_F. Substitution of the above solution into equations [6.49] and [6.2] gives:

$$F_1 - k_2(X_{1F} - X_{2F}) - k_1 X_{1F} = -m_1 \omega_F^2 X_{1F}, \tag{6.50}$$
$$k_2(X_{1F} - X_{2F}) = -m_2 \omega_F^2 X_{2F}. \tag{6.51}$$

Equation [6.51] may be written as:

$$X_{2F}/X_{1F} = k_2/(k_2 - m_2 \omega_F^2). \tag{6.52}$$

From equations [6.50] and [6.52] one obtains

$$F_1 - k_2[X_{1F} - \{k_2/(k_2 - m_2 \omega_F^2)\}X_{1F}] - k_1 X_{1F} = -m_1 \omega_F^2 X_{1F}$$

or

$$X_{1F} = F_1/[-m_1 \omega_F^2 + k_1 + k_2 - k_2^2/(k_2 - m_2 \omega_F^2)]$$

and from equation [6.52]:

$$X_{2F} = F_1 k_2/\{(-m_1 \omega_F^2 + k_1 + k_2)(k_2 - m_2 \omega_F^2) - k_2^2\}.$$

It should be noted that $X_{1F} = 0$ if

$$1/[-m_1 \omega_F^2 + k_1 + k_2 - k_2^2/(k_2 - m_2 \omega_F^2)] = 0$$

or

$$(k_2 - m_2\omega_F^2)/\{(k_2 - m_2\omega_F^2)(k_1 + k_2 - m_1\omega_F^2) - k_2^2\} = 0.$$

This condition is satisfied when $\omega_F^2 = k_2/m_2$. Thus body 1 does not oscillate and the whole energy of the vibration is associated with body 2. This is the principle of the dynamic vibration absorber. In this device body 1 could represent some machine that is subjected to harmful vibrations with a circular frequency ω_F. If a small body (body 2) of mass m_2 equal to k_2/ω_F^2 is attached to the machine by a spring of stiffness k_2, then the amplitude of the vibrations of the machine should be reduced to zero. Such a device would normally incorporate damping as well.

Example 6.7
Dynamic model of a pile driver

A vibration pile driver which is used to drive a pile P into the ground is shown in Figure 6.19. The source of the forced vibrations is a vertical force, due to rotating out-of-balance masses in box G, of magnitude $40\omega^2 \sin \omega t$ N, where ω is the rotational speed in rad/s of the masses located in G.

The box G is attached to the pile by a chuck H in such a way that G, H and P can be regarded as a rigid body of mass 8000 kg. The yoke CD is a rigid body of mass 1000 kg. All other masses may be neglected.

The springs AB have a combined stiffness of 100 kN/m. The links CE and DF have together an effective vertical stiffness of 2000 kN/m. The soil into which the pile is driven can be regarded as having a linear stiffness of 200 kN/m.

Consider point A to be fixed.

Construct a dynamic model for the system, and hence for steady-state conditions estimate the amplitude of the displacement of the pile and the amplitude of the force in the soil when $\omega = 100$ rad/s. Comment on the limitations of the model used.

Solution The dynamic model for the pile driver is shown in Figure 6.20(a). It has two degrees of freedom. The vibration box G and pile P form a rigid body which we assume to have a displacement y_1 upwards from the equilibrium position. The yoke CD forms another rigid mass which has a displacement y_2, say, upwards. Let $y_1 > y_2$. The free-body diagrams for the two rigid bodies are shown in Figure 6.20(b).

The equations of motion for the two rigid bodies are shown below.

$$-2000 \times 10^3(y_1 - y_2) - 200 \times 10^3 y_1 + 40\omega^2 \sin \omega t = 8000\ddot{y}_1,$$
$$-100 \times 10^3 y_2 + 2000 \times 10^3(y_1 - y_2) = 1000\ddot{y}_2.$$

The solution may be assumed in the form:

$$y_1 = A \sin \omega t \qquad \text{and} \qquad y_2 = B \sin \omega t.$$

Therefore,

$$-2000(A - B) - 200A + 0.04\omega^2 = -8\omega^2 A \qquad [6.53]$$

and

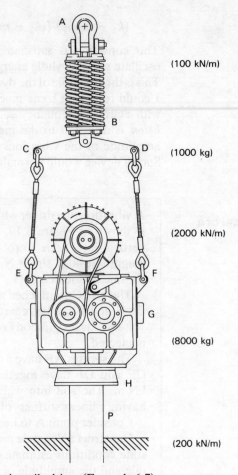

(100 kN/m)

(1000 kg)

(2000 kN/m)

(8000 kg)

(200 kN/m)

Figure 6.19   Vibration pile driver (Example 6.7).

$$-100B + 2000(A - B) = -\omega^2 B. \qquad [6.54]$$

From equation [6.54] we obtain:

$$B = 2000A/(2100 - \omega^2). \qquad [6.55]$$

Substitution of B in equation [6.53] gives:

$$(8\omega^2 - 2200)A + 2000^2 A/(2100 - \omega^2) + 0.04\omega^2 = 0.$$

Hence

$$A = \{-0.04\omega^2(2100 - \omega^2)\}/\{-8\omega^4 + 19 \times 10^3 \omega^2 - 620 \times 10^3\}.$$

If $\omega^2 = 10^4$, then

$$A = \{-0.04 \times 10^4(-7900)\}/\{-8 \times 10^8 + 1.9 \times 10^8 \\ - 0.0062 \times 10^8\}$$

or

$$A = -5.175 \times 10^{-3}\,\text{m} = -5.175\,\text{mm}.$$

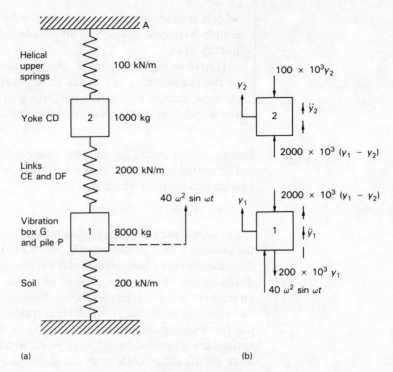

Figure 6.20 (a) Dynamic model of pile driver; (b) Free-body diagrams for pile driver.

The negative sign occurs because the displacement of body 1 is out of phase by 180° with the applied excitation force. Thus

$$y_1 = -5.175 \sin \omega t = 5.175 \sin (\omega t - \pi) \text{ mm}.$$

Finally, we can obtain the amplitude of the force acting in the soil which amounts to $200 \times 5.175 = 1035 \text{ N}$.

Defects of the model: the pile probably needs to be regarded as a continuous structure with distributed mass and elasticity, the soil is unlikely to have a linear stiffness and its damping effect will also be important. The point A is unlikely to be at a fixed spatial position during oscillations.

Answers   The amplitude of the displacement of the pile is **5.18 mm** and the amplitude of the force in the soil is **1035 N.**

Example 6.8 **Steady-state forced vibration of automobile body**	The sprung mass of an automobile is 1000 kg, its mass centre G is midway between the front and rear axles which are 2.5 m apart, and its moment of inertia about the pitching axis through G is 2083 kg m². The suspension springs have a total stiffness of 4000 N/m at the rear, and a total stiffness of 2000 N/m at the front. The automobile is mounted on a testing machine which holds the rear

wheels stationary but which moves the front wheels vertically with simple harmonic motion of amplitude 0.5 cm and a circular frequency of ω.

Derive an expression for θ', the amplitude of the pitching angle θ of the automobile, due to the steady-state forced vibration only. Assume that $\sin \theta \simeq \theta$, that the tyres are rigid, and that the axes of the suspension springs remain in the vertical position.

Solution The model for the automobile is shown in Figure 6.21.

The testing machine gives the front wheels a displacement y_m from the equilibrium position which is:

$$y_m = 5 \times 10^{-3} \sin \omega t \text{ m}.$$

Let us assume that this displacement is downwards in the direction of the positive y axis, as shown in Figure 6.22. The automobile body is also displaced; let the displacement of the centre of mass be y_G and the angular displacement of the vehicle be θ, as shown in Figure 6.22. The upper attachment points of the springs are displaced downwards by $y_G + 1.25\theta$ and $y_G - 1.25\theta$, for the front and rear springs, respectively. In the case of the front springs let us assume that $y_m > y_G + 1.25\theta$. Thus the front springs are extended by $y_m - y_G - 1.25\theta$ and the front springs exert a force on the automobile body, as shown in Figure 6.22. Relative to the equilibrium position, the rear springs are compressed by $y_G - 1.25\theta$ and a force acts upwards on the body.

The equations of motion for the body are:

$$\Sigma F_y = m\ddot{y}_G,$$
$$\Sigma M_G = I_G\ddot{\theta}$$

or

$$2000(y_m - y_G - 1.25\theta) - 4000(y_G - 1.25\theta) = 1000\ddot{y}_G$$

and

$$1.25 \times 2000(y_m - y_G - 1.25\theta) + 1.25 \times 4000(y_G - 1.25\theta)$$
$$= 2083\ddot{\theta}.$$

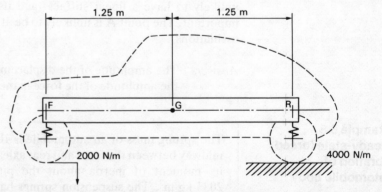

Figure 6.21 Automobile body mounted on vehicle testing machine (Example 6.8).

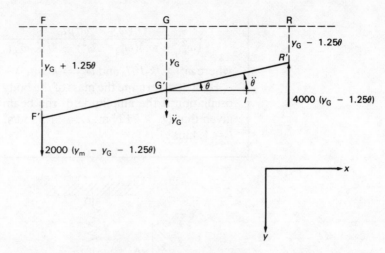

Figure 6.22 Free-body diagram for automobile body. (FGR is equilibrium position, F'G'R' is instantaneous position).

After substituting for y_m we obtain:

$$\ddot{y}_G + 6y_G - 2.5\theta = 10^{-2} \sin \omega t \qquad [6.56]$$

and

$$\ddot{\theta} - 1.2y_G + 4.5\theta = 6 \times 10^{-3} \sin \omega t. \qquad [6.57]$$

The solution of the system of equations [6.56] and [6.57] may be assumed to be:

$$y_G = Y_G \sin \omega t \qquad \text{and} \qquad \theta = \theta' \sin \omega t$$

and leads to equations:

$$-\omega^2 Y_G + 6Y_G - 2.5\theta' = 10^{-2},$$
$$-\omega^2 \theta' - 1.2Y_G + 4.5\theta' = 0.6 \times 10^{-2}.$$

Elimination of Y_G from the two above equations leads to:

$$\theta' = \{(0.006\omega^2 - 0.048)/(-\omega^4 + 10.5\omega^2 - 24)\} \text{ [rad]}$$

which is the expression required in the problem.

Example 6.9
Beam excited by couple

Figure 6.23 shows a rigid beam ABC which is freely hinged at A and suspended at its mid-point B by a spring BD of stiffness k_1. A body E of mass m is suspended from the beam by a spring CE of stiffness k_2, and the beam is horizontal in the static equilibrium position. The moment of inertia of the beam about the rotation axis through A is I_0.

Show that, when the couple with moment $Q_0 \cos \omega t$, where ω is a constant, is applied to the beam, the amplitude of the small angular oscillations of the beam is equal to

$$\frac{Q_0(\omega_{n2}^2 - \omega^2)/I_0}{(\omega_{n1}^2 - \omega^2)(\omega_{n2}^2 - \omega^2) - 4l^2k_2\omega^2/I_0},$$

where $\omega_{n1}^2 = k_1l^2/I_0$ and $\omega_{n2}^2 = k_2/m$.

Hence, determine the mass of the body E and the amplitude of its oscillation if the amplitude of the beam oscillation is to be zero, given that $Q_0 = 71$ N m, $\omega = 11.5$ rad/s, $k_2 = 0.6 \times 10^4$ N/m, and $l = 1.4$ m.

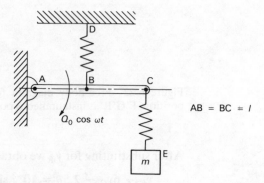

Figure 6.23   Diagram for Example 6.9.

Solution   The free-body diagrams for the beam ABC and the body E are shown in Figure 6.24. θ is the angular displacement of the beam from its equilibrium position in a clockwise sense and y is the downwards displacement of E, which is assumed to be less than the displacement of C.

The equations of motion describing the motion of the beam ABC and the body E are:

$$-2lk_2(2l\theta - y) - k_1l^2\theta + Q_0 \cos \omega t = I_0\ddot{\theta},$$
$$k_2(2l\theta - y) = m\ddot{y}.$$

Rearranging the two above equations we have:

$$I_0\ddot{\theta} - 2k_2ly + (4k_2l^2 + k_1l^2)\theta = Q_0 \cos \omega t,$$
$$m\ddot{y} + k_2y - 2k_2l\theta = 0.$$

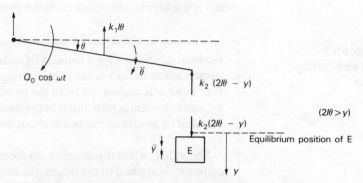

Figure 6.24   Free-body diagrams for Example 6.9.

Let us assume that

$$y = Y \cos \omega t \quad \text{and} \quad \theta = X \cos \omega t.$$

Thus

$$-I_0 \omega^2 X - 2k_2 lY + (4k_2 l^2 + k_1 l^2)X = Q_0, \qquad [6.58]$$
$$-m\omega^2 Y + k_2 Y - 2k_2 lX = 0. \qquad [6.59]$$

After obtaining an expression for Y from equation [6.59] and substituting into equation [6.58], we obtain:

$$-I_0 \omega^2 X - 2k_2 l\{2k_2 lX/(k_2 - m\omega^2)\} + (4k_2 l^2 + k_1 l^2)X = Q_0.$$

Hence,

$$X = \frac{Q_0(k_2 - m\omega^2)}{-\omega^2(k_2 - m\omega^2)I_0 - 4k_2^2 l^2 + (4k_2 l^2 + k_1 l^2)(k_2 - m\omega^2)}.$$

After some algebraic manipulation and after using

$$\omega_{n1}^2 = k_1 l^2/I_0 \quad \text{and} \quad \omega_{n2}^2 = k_2/m$$

we find that:

$$X = \frac{Q_0(\omega_{n2}^2 - \omega^2)/I_0}{\omega^2(\omega^2 - \omega_{n2}^2) - (4k_2 l^2/I_0)\omega_{n2}^2 + (4k_2 l^2/I_0 + \omega_{n1}^2)(\omega_{n2}^2 - \omega^2)}.$$

Further algebraic arrangement leads to the expression for X in the required form:

$$X = \frac{Q_0(\omega_{n2}^2 - \omega^2)/I_0}{(\omega_{n1}^2 - \omega^2)(\omega_{n2}^2 - \omega^2) - 4l^2 k_2 \omega^2/I_0}.$$

We know that $Q_0 = 71$ [N m], $\omega = 11.5$ [rad/s], $k_2 = 0.6 \times 10^4$ [N/m], $l = 1.4$ [m]. Thus:

$$\omega_{n1}^2 = k_1 \times 1.4^2/I_0 \quad \text{and} \quad \omega_{n2}^2 = 0.6 \times 10^4/m.$$

If $X = 0$, then $\omega^2 = k_2/m$ or $0.6 \times 10^4/m - 11.5^2 = 0$. And

$$m = 0.6 \times 10^4/11.5^2 = 45.37 \text{ [kg]}.$$

The amplitude of oscillations of the body E is obtained from equation [6.58], in this case with $X = 0$:

$$-2k_2 lY = Q_0.$$

Hence

$$Y = -71/(2 \times 0.6 \times 10^4 \times 1.4) = -4.226 \times 10^{-3} \text{ [m]}.$$

It should be noted that the negative sign in the expression for Y indicates that at this frequency the body E has an upward motion when the beam is deflected in a clockwise angular sense.

Answer Mass of body E for the case when the beam oscillation has zero amplitude is **45.4 kg** and the amplitude of vibration of the body E in this case is **4.23 mm**.

6.2 Transverse vibrations of beams

The stiffness of a beam with a single concentrated load has been discussed in Example 1.1. Beams with two concentrated loads will now be considered. A massless shaft with two rotors could be regarded as a beam system in which the shaft is either built-in at the bearings or simply supported, if the bearings are self-aligning. Solution of these vibration problems requires information on the deflection of beams which may be found, for example, in *Strength of Materials and Structures* by J. Case and A. H. Chilver, Edward Arnold 1971. In Example 6.10 the bending moment of a sagging beam will be considered as positive. Also the downwards deflection of the beam will be treated as positive. If we define an xy co-ordinate system (see Figure 6.26) with the origin O at the left-hand end of the beam, then the following relationship holds:

$$EI \, d^2y/dx^2 = -M,$$

where M is the bending moment at a section at a distance x from O, E is Young's modulus and I is the second moment of area of the beam about a transverse axis ($I = \pi d^4/64$ for a solid circular beam). $y(x)$ characterizes the shape of the beam during bending.

**Example 6.10
Free vibrations of a
loaded beam**

A uniform, light shaft can be regarded as being simply supported in its bearings. It is loaded with two rotors as shown in Figure 6.25. The shaft diameter is 50 mm and Young's modulus for the shaft is $0.21 \times 10^{12} \, \text{N/m}^2$. Determine:

(a) the two natural frequencies of vibration, and
(b) the modal shapes of the shaft vibrations at these frequencies.

Assuming that the rotors are concentrated masses attached to the massless shaft, use an exact method to solve for (a) and (b).

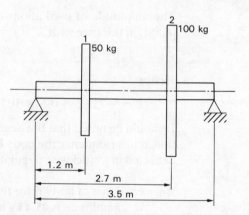

Figure 6.25   Model of loaded beam (Example 6.10).

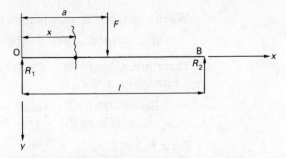

Figure 6.26   Free-body diagram for the beam loaded at a single point.

Solution   Figure 6.26 shows a simply supported beam of length l with a concentrated load F at a distance a from the left-hand beam support, the origin of the co-ordinate system. R_1 and R_2 denote the forces acting on the beam at the support points.

Let us consider the bending moment M at a distance x along the beam from the co-ordinate system origin. For $x \leqslant a$,

$$M = R_1x = Fx(l - a)/l \qquad \text{as} \qquad R_1 = F(l - a)/l.$$

For $a \leqslant x \leqslant l$,

$$M = R_1x - F(x - a).$$

$$EI\, d^2y/dx^2 = -M.$$

Therefore

$$EI\, d^2y/dx^2 = -R_1x + F(x - a) \qquad \text{for } a \leqslant x \leqslant l$$

and

$$EI\, d^2y/dx^2 = -R_1x \qquad \text{for } x \leqslant a.$$

Hence for $a \leqslant x \leqslant l$:

$$EI\, dy/dx = -R_1x^2/2 + F(x - a)^2/2 + C_1$$

and

$$EIy = -R_1x^3/6 + F(x - a)^3/6 + C_1x + C_2. \qquad [6.60]$$

For $x \leqslant a$ we have:

$$EIy = -R_1x^3/6 + C_3x + C_4.$$

Thus we have two expressions for y, one for $x \leqslant a$ and the other for $a \leqslant x \leqslant l$. These two expressions must have the same value of y at $x = a$. Similarly, we must have the same value for dy/dx at $x = a$. Hence $C_1 = C_3$ and $C_2 = C_4$. Finally, we may write for $x \leqslant a$:

$$EIy = -R_1x^3/6 + C_1x + C_2. \qquad [6.61]$$

When $x = 0$, $y = 0$ and from equation [6.61], we have

$$C_2 = 0.$$

When $x = l$, $y = 0$ and equation [6.60] leads to:

$$0 = -R_1 l^3/6 + F(l - a)^3/6 + C_1 l.$$

Therefore, $C_1 = Fbl/6 - Fb^3/(6l)$, where $b = l - a$.
Finally, for $x \leq a$,

$$Ely = -Fbx^3/6l + Fblx/6 - Fb^3x/6l$$
$$= (Fbx/6l)(l^2 - x^2 - b^2). \qquad [6.62]$$

For $a \leq x \leq l$

$$Ely = -Fbx^3/6l + F(x - a)^3/6 + Fblx/6 - Fb^3x/6l$$
$$= (Fbx/6l)(l^2 - x^2 - b^2) + F(x - a)^3/6. \qquad [6.63]$$

Let us consider a beam that is loaded by discrete weights located at several points. As the system is linear, the deflection of the beam from its equilibrium position at a chosen point on the beam may be found by addition of the deflections caused at this point by each load independently.

When the shaft is vibrating at a circular frequency ω_n let the shaft deflection be y_1 at the point where the 50 kg rotor is attached ($x = 1.2$ m) and y_2 at the point of attachment of the 100 kg rotor ($x = 2.7$ m). Then the relations between the magnitudes of the forces acting on the beam (shaft) and the displacements caused by them are:

$$\begin{aligned} \text{at} \quad x &= 1.2 \text{ m} & F_1 &= 50y_1\omega_n^2 & \text{and} \\ \text{at} \quad x &= 2.7 \text{ m} & F_2 &= 100y_2\omega_n^2. \end{aligned}$$

The system is linear, so the deflections at $x = 1.2$ m may be found by addition of the deflections caused at this point by the two separate loads located at $x = a_1 = 1.2$ m and at $x = a_2 = 2.7$ m.

Let the deflection at $x = 1.2$ m caused by load F_1 located at $x = a_1 = 1.2$ m be y_{11}, and let the deflection at $x = 1.2$ m caused by load F_2 located at the point $x = a_2 = 2.7$ m be y_{12}.

Let the deflection at $x = 2.7$ m caused by load F_1 at $x = a_1 = 1.2$ m be y_{21}, and let the deflection at $x = 2.7$ m caused by load F_2 at $x = a_2 = 2.7$ m be y_{22}.

Then the deflections at the point $x = 1.2$ m and at the point $x = 2.7$ m are respectively;

$$y_1 = y_{11} + y_{12} \qquad \text{and} \qquad y_2 = y_{21} + y_{22}.$$

y_{11}, y_{12} and y_{22} may be found from equation [6.62]. Thus

$$Ely_{11} = \{2.3 \times 1.2F_1/(6 \times 3.5)\}\{3.5^2 - 1.2^2 - 2.3^2\}$$
$$= 0.72549F_1,$$
$$Ely_{12} = \{0.8 \times 1.2F_2/(6 \times 3.5)\}\{3.5^2 - 1.2^2 - 0.8^2\}$$
$$= 0.46491F_2,$$
$$Ely_{22} = \{0.8 \times 2.7F_2/(6 \times 3.5)\}\{3.5^2 - 2.7^2 - 0.8^2\}$$
$$= 0.44434F_2.$$

y_{21} is determined from equation [6.63].

$$EIy_{21} = \{2.7 \times 2.3 \times F_1/(6 \times 3.5)\}\{3.5^2 - 2.7^2 - 2.3^2\}$$
$$+ (2.7 - 1.2)^3 F_1/6$$
$$= 0.46491 F_1.$$

We know that:

$$y_1 = y_{11} + y_{12} \quad \text{and} \quad y_2 = y_{21} + y_{22};$$

hence

$$EIy_1 = 0.72549 F_1 + 0.46491 F_2, \tag{6.64}$$
$$EIy_2 = 0.46491 F_1 + 0.44434 F_2 \tag{6.65}$$

and since $F_1 = 50 y_1 \omega_n^2$ and $F_2 = 100 y_2 \omega_n^2$,

$$EIy_1 = 0.72549 \times 50 y_1 \omega_n^2 + 0.46491 \times 100 y_2 \omega_n^2,$$
$$EIy_2 = 0.46491 \times 50 y_1 \omega_n^2 + 0.44434 \times 100 y_2 \omega_n^2.$$

Hence,

$$EIy_1/\omega_n^2 = 36.2745 y_1 + 46.491 y_2,$$
$$EIy_2/\omega_n^2 = 23.2455 y_1 + 44.434 y_2.$$

Hence

$$(EI/\omega_n^2 - 44.434) y_2 = 23.2455 y_1 \tag{6.66}$$

and

$$(EI/\omega_n^2 - 36.2745) y_1 = 46.491 y_2. \tag{6.67}$$

Therefore from equations [6.66] and [6.67] we obtain:

$$(EI/\omega_n^2 - 44.434)(EI/\omega_n^2 - 36.2745) = 23.2455 \times 46.491.$$

Finally, the following quadratic equation in ω_n^2 may be obtained:

$$\omega_n^4/(EI)^2 - 0.15196 \omega_n^2/EI + 1.88283 \times 10^{-3} = 0.$$

As

$$EI = 0.21 \times 10^{12} \times \pi(50 \times 10^{-3})^4/64 = 6.44272 \times 10^4$$

$$\omega_n^4 - 9.79036 \times 10^3 \omega_n^2 + 7.81537 \times 10^6 = 0.$$

Thus

$$\omega_n^2 = 4.89518 \times 10^3 \mp (23.9628 \times 10^6 - 7.81537 \times 10^6)^{0.5}.$$

Hence

$$\omega_{n1}^2 = 876.79 \quad \text{and} \quad \omega_{n2}^2 = 8913.57.$$
$$\omega_{n1} = 29.61 \text{ rad/s} \quad \text{and} \quad \omega_{n2} = 94.41 \text{ rad/s}.$$
$$f_{n1} = 4.713 \text{ Hz} \quad \text{and} \quad f_{n2} = 15.03 \text{ Hz}.$$

Answer to part (a) The natural frequencies are **4.71 Hz** and **15.03 Hz**.

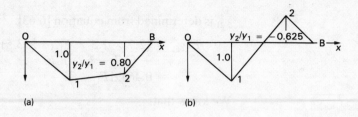

(a)   (b)

Figure 6.27 Modal shapes of vibration for the beam. (a) mode 1: $f_1 = 4.71$ Hz. (b) mode 2: $f_2 = 15.03$ Hz.

Next, equation [6.66] is used to find the modal shapes of the vibration. For the first mode of vibration $\omega_{n1}^2 = 876.79$ and from

$$(EI/\omega_{n1}^2 - 44.434)y_2 = 23.2455y_1$$

one obtains

$$y_2/y_1 = 0.800.$$

For the second mode of vibration when $\omega_{n2}^2 = 8913.57$

$$y_2/y_1 = -0.625.$$

The modal shapes of vibration of the shaft are shown in Figure 6.27.

6.3 Rayleigh's method applied to beams with concentrated loads

In Rayleigh's method a deflection shape for the vibrating beam is assumed to be known. The deflection shape of the beam at static equilibrium could be used in the calculations. If y_1 is the static deflection of a light beam at position 1, where the load of mass m_1 is located, and y_2 is the static deflection at station 2, where the load of mass m_2 is located, then T_{max}, the maximum kinetic energy of the system (vibrating with the natural circular frequency ω_n), is given by:

$$T_{max} = 0.5\omega_n^2(m_1y_1^2 + m_2y_2^2).$$

Similarly, V_{max}, the maximum of the total potential energy of the system in relation to the equilibrium position of the system in a gravitational field is expressed by:

$$V_{max} = 0.5(m_1gy_1 + m_2gy_2).$$

Equation [4.5] is:

$$T_{max} = V_{max}.$$

Hence

$$\omega_n^2 = g(m_1y_1 + m_2y_2)/(m_1y_1^2 + m_2y_2^2). \qquad [6.68]$$

This method is particularly useful when applied to beams with several concentrated masses. In the case of p discrete masses in the system the following formula is used:

$$\omega_n^2 = g\left(\sum_{q=1}^{p} m_q y_q\right)\Bigg/\left(\sum_{q=1}^{p} m_q y_q^2\right),$$

Rayleigh's method will give an approximation for the lowest natural frequency which will be greater than that obtained by an exact method based on the dynamic shape of the deflected beam. It should be noted that for a system with many concentrated masses the analytical method (see Example 6.10), which requires a knowledge of the dynamic beam shape, may be very laborious, and therefore Rayleigh's method may be more convenient.

Example 6.11 **Rayleigh's method**	Obtain an estimate of the lowest natural frequency for the system described in Example 6.10 using Rayleigh's method.

Solution   Equations [6.64] and [6.65] may be used, as in Example 6.10, to obtain expressions for the beam deflections. The shaft (beam) is loaded with two rotors, then $F_1 = 50g$ and $F_2 = 100g$. Hence we can obtain the static deflection shape of the beam:

$$EIy_1 = 0.72549 \times 50g + 0.46491 \times 100g$$
$$= 82.7655g.$$
$$EIy_2 = 0.46491 \times 50g + 0.44434 \times 100g$$
$$= 67.6795g.$$

From equation [6.68]:

$$\omega_n^2 = EI(50 \times 82.7655 + 100 \times 67.6795)/(50 \times 82.7655^2$$
$$+ 100 \times 67.6795^2)$$
$$= 6.44272 \times 10^4(4138.275 + 6767.95)/(342506.4 + 458051.5)$$
$$= 877.710.$$

Hence $\omega_n = 29.63$ rad/s and $f_n = 4.716$ Hz. The estimate for the lowest natural frequency is only slightly greater than that obtained by the exact method and is clearly a good estimate.

Answer   The estimate for the lowest natural frequency by Rayleigh's method is **4.72 Hz.**

Problems

6.1   (a)   Calculate the natural frequencies and the mode shapes for the system shown in Figure 6.28. Both bodies A and B are of mass 10 kg. All the springs are of stiffness 1 kN/m.

(b)   B is held and A is displaced 20 mm to the right. If both bodies are released simultaneously, derive expressions for the displacements describing the resulting motion.

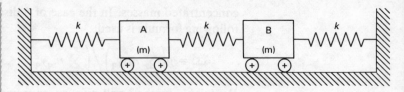

Figure 6.28   Diagram for Problem 6.1. $k = 1000$ N/m and $m = 10$ kg.

Answers   (a) 1.59 Hz, 2.76 Hz; (1, 1), (1, −1)
          (b) $x_A = 10(\cos 10t + \cos 17.32t)$ mm
               $x_B = 10(\cos 10t − \cos 17.32t)$ mm

6.2   Consider the system shown in Figure 6.29. It consists of two
bodies of masses 1 kg and 2 kg hanging on two springs of stiffness
40 N/m and 80 N m.

   Determine for the system:
   (a)   the natural frequencies,
   (b)   the mode shapes, and
   (c)   the positions of the nodes in relation to the equilibrium
positions of the bodies, assuming that the distance between the two
bodies at equilibrium is 1 m.

Answers   (a) 0.521 Hz, 1.945 Hz (b) (1, 1.366), (1, −0.366) (c)
          mode 1; node is 2.732 m from the equilibrium position of
          body 1 and 3.732 m from the equilibrium position of
          body 2: mode 2; node is 0.732 m from equilibrium
          position of body 1 and 0.268 m from body 2.

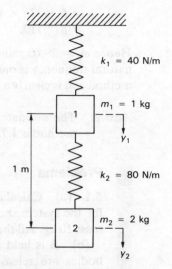

Figure 6.29   Diagram for Problem 6.2.

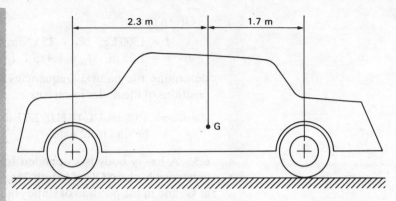

Figure 6.30   Diagram for Problem 6.3.

6.3   Figure 6.30 shows a schematic diagram of a motor vehicle. The mass of the vehicle is 6000 kg and the moment of inertia about an axis through the centre of mass G, perpendicular to the section shown in Figure 6.30, is 15 000 kg m^2. The equivalent stiffness of the tyres and springs at the front of the vehicle is 4.8×10^5 N/m and the equivalent stiffness at the rear wheels is 5×10^5 N/m.

By regarding the vehicle as a beam supported by two springs, determine the natural frequencies of small amplitude oscillations of the vehicle. Estimate the position of the node for the lowest natural frequency.

Answers   1.99 Hz and 2.63 Hz, 4.13 m in front of the front wheels.

6.4   A stationary vehicle has a wheelbase $(l_1 + l_2)$, with the centre of mass G located at a distance l_1 behind the axis of the front wheels. The vehicle has a mass M, and its radius of gyration about the horizontal axis passing through G is r. The stiffnesses of the front and rear springs are, respectively, k_1 and k_2.

Draw an appropriate free-body diagram and write down the equations of motion for the vehicle when undergoing pitching vibration, assuming that displacements are small and in the vertical plane, and that G moves vertically. Neglect the effects due to the tyres and shock absorbers.

Let

$a = (k_1 + k_2)/M,$
$b = k_1 k_2 (l_1 + l_2)^2/(M^2 r^2)$ and
$c = (k_1 l_1^2 + k_2 l_2^2)/(Mr^2).$

Hence show that the angular frequencies of the modes of vibration for pitching motion of the vehicle may be found from the equation:

$$\omega^4 - (a + c)\omega^2 + b = 0.$$

Given that:

$$M = 1500\,\text{kg}, \quad k_1 = 35\,\text{kN/m}, \quad k_2 = 38\,\text{kN/m},$$
$$r = 1.25\,\text{m}, \quad l_1 = 1.4\,\text{m}, \quad l_2 = 1.7\,\text{m},$$

determine the natural frequencies of pitching vibration and the positions of the nodes in each case.

Answers   1.08 and 1.41 Hz; 2.77 m behind rear axle and 1.05 m behind front axle.

6.5   A heavy body is suspended from a fixed point O by a light inextensible chain OC of length 2 m. The mass centre of the body is at G, and in the position of static equilibrium OG = 5 m.

The body is then allowed to swing as a pendulum with the points O, C and G in a vertical plane. Given that the radius of gyration of the body about the horizontal axis through G perpendicular to this plane is 2.5 m, determine the possible frequencies of small oscillations.

Answers   0.196 Hz, 0.620 Hz.

6.6   A beam of length 3 m is supported horizontally from a floor by two vertical springs, each of stiffness 300 kN/m, one being placed at each end. Because of the presence of adjacent machinery the floor is oscillating with simple harmonic motion at a frequency of 4 Hz. The moment of inertia of the beam about a rotation axis through G, the mass centre of the beam, is 2500 kg m². G is midway between the supports.

Determine the stiffness of an additional spring, placed co-axially with one of the spring supports between the beam and the floor, such that G has no motion in an absolute system.

Answer   122.7 kN/m.

6.7   Figure 6.31 shows a steel shaft with two rotors A and B at its ends. The rotor A has a moment of inertia of 0.1 kg m² and rotor B

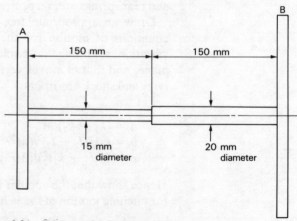

Figure 6.31   Diagram for Problem 6.7.

has a moment of inertia of 0.2 kg m^2, both about the axis of rotation of the shaft. The shaft joining the two rotors comprises two parts: a solid circular shaft of length 150 mm and diameter 15 mm and a second solid shaft of length 150 mm and diameter 20 mm, as shown in Figure 6.31.

Determine (a) the natural frequency of torsional oscillations and (b) the position of the node.

The modulus of rigidity of steel is $85 \times 10^9 \text{ Pa}$.

Answers (a) 28.51 Hz, (b) 131.64 mm from A.

6.8 A shunting locomotive pushes a truck which later moves separately until the moment of impact with another truck standing on the same line. Just before impact the moving truck has a velocity v and both trucks couple during impact. The initially stationary truck has a mass m_1 and the second truck has mass m_2. The stiffness of the buffer of the first truck amounts to k_1 and the stiffness of the buffer of the second truck is k_2.

(a) Determine the circular natural frequencies and the modes of vibration for the system.

(b) Derive expressions for the displacements of both trucks.

(c) Find the displacements of both trucks, five seconds after impact, assuming that $m_1 = 25\,000$ kg, $m_2 = 30\,000$ kg, $k_1 = 4$ MN/m, $k_2 = 6$ MN/m and the velocity v of the initially moving truck is 10 km/h.

Answers (a) $0, [k_1 k_2 (m_1 + m_2)/\{(k_1 + k_2)m_1 m_2\}]^{0.5}$;
$(1, 1), (1, -m_1/m_2)$
(b) $x_1 = [-vm_2/\{\omega(m_1 + m_2)\}] \sin \omega t + vm_2 t/(m_1 + m_2)$
and
$x_2 = [vm_1/\{\omega(m_1 + m_2)\}] \sin \omega t + vm_2 t/(m_1 + m_2)$,
where $\omega = [k_1 k_2 (m_1 + m_2)/\{(k_1 + k_2)m_1 m_2\}]^{0.5}$
(c) 7.616 m and 7.542 m.

6.9 A machine of mass 4000 kg is supported on elastic mountings at A and B which have stiffnesses of 200 kN/m and 600 kN/m, respectively (see Figure 6.32). The mass centre of the machine is at G and the radius of gyration of the machine about the horizontal axis through G, perpendicular to the plane containing the axes of the mountings, is 0.5 m.

Initially the machine is at rest. It then receives a vertical blow of very short duration at E, the time integral of the blow being 350 N s.

Assuming:

(a) that the motion of the machine takes place in a vertical plane,

(b) that the angular displacement θ of the machine is small so that $\sin \theta \simeq \theta$,

(c) that the axes of the mountings remain vertical, and

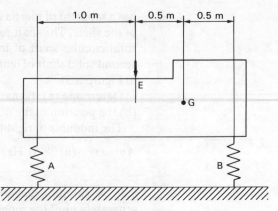

Figure 6.32   Diagram for Problem 6.9.

(d)   that the damping is very small,

derive an expression for the force in mounting A at time t after the blow.

Answer $F_A = 1237.4 \sin 14.14t + 2143.3 \sin 24.49t$ N.

6.10   A reciprocating aircraft engine drives a propeller through a reduction gear of ratio 5:3. The rotating parts of the engine have a moment of inertia of 20 kg m² and the moment of inertia of the propeller is 92 kg m².

The shaft between the crank and the gears is 230 mm long, has an external diameter of 100 mm and an internal diameter of 50 mm. The shaft between the gears and the propeller is 300 mm long, has an external diameter of 115 mm and an internal diameter of 64 mm.

Determine:

(a)   the natural frequency of the system,

(b)   the position of the node.

Given that the engine torque fluctuation is 200 cos 200t N m, where t is the time in seconds, find also

(c)   the amplitudes of torsional oscillations set up in the engine and propeller.

The modulus of rigidity of the material of the shaft is 8.3 × 10¹⁰ N/m².

Answers   (a) 46.3 Hz (b) 165.5 mm from the propeller
(c) 107.1 × 10⁻⁶ rad and 45.7 × 10⁻⁶ rad.

6.11   Figure 6.33 shows part of a hydraulic circuit for a marine diesel engine. Spool valve A moves in the sleeve B under the influence of spring S_2, and controls the flow of oil through ports C. The sleeve moves in a fixed casing under the influence of spring S_1. Under certain operating conditions the sleeve B may be subjected

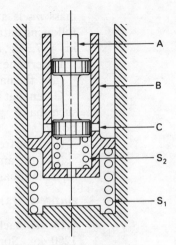

Figure 6.33   Diagram for Problem 6.11.

to axial impact loading. Details of the circuit elements are given below:

mass of spool valve A = 0.5 kg,
mass of sleeve B = 1.0 kg,
stiffness of spring S_1 = 3.2 kN/m, and
stiffness of spring S_2 = 1.6 kN/m.

The sleeve B is subjected to an axial blow of short duration at its upper end, the time integral of the blow being 0.5 N s.

(a)   Determine the natural frequencies and the natural modes of vibration of the system.

(b)   Derive an expression for the relative displacement between the valve and the sleeve at any time t after the blow.

Damping in the system is to be neglected.

Answers   (a)   6.37, 12.73 Hz; (1, 2), (1, −1)
(b)   (1/240) sin 40t − (1/120) sin 80t m.

6.12   In the system shown in Figure 6.34, body 1 of mass m_1 is attached by a spring of stiffness k_1 to a rigid support and body 2 of

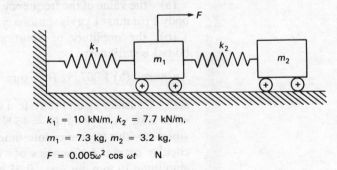

k_1 = 10 kN/m, k_2 = 7.7 kN/m,
m_1 = 7.3 kg, m_2 = 3.2 kg,
F = 0.005ω^2 cos ωt N

Figure 6.34   Diagram for Problem 6.12.

mass m_2 is attached to body 1 by a spring of stiffness k_2. The following data apply:

$m_1 = 7.3$ kg, $m_2 = 3.2$ kg, $k_1 = 10$ kN/m, and $k_2 = 7.7$ kN/m.

Determine:

(a)   the natural frequencies.

Given that a force F is applied to body 1, as shown in the diagram, such that $F = 0.005\omega^2 \cos \omega t$ N, determine for steady-state vibrations:

(b)   the frequency at which the body of mass m_1 is stationary, and

(c)   the amplitude of motion of the body of mass m_2 when mass m_1 is stationary.

Answers   (a) 4.56 Hz, 10.08 Hz (b) 7.81 Hz (c) 1.56 mm.

6.13   A machine of mass 44 kg is mounted on a base plate of mass 1250 kg. Spring supports of stiffness 50 kN/m are interposed between the machine and the base plate. When the machine and base plate were installed it was noted that the supporting joists deflected by an amount 2.5 mm. A vertical harmonic force 12 sin ωt N is generated by the machine, where ω is the crankshaft speed in rad/s.

Assuming that only vertical vibrations take place and the damping is negligible, obtain expressions for the amplitudes of steady-state forced vibration of the machine and of the base plate. Hence calculate:

(a)   the value of ω at which the machine has zero amplitude of vibration;

(b)   the amplitude of steady-state forced vibration of the base plate when the condition in (a) is reached.

Answers   (a) 10.19 Hz (b) 0.24 mm.

6.14   A system of two bodies and two springs is as shown in Figure 6.35, where $m_1 = 1$ kg, $m_2 = 2$ kg, $k_1 = 40$ N/m and $k_2 = 80$ N/m. The upper spring is connected to a vibrating plate support P which has a displacement described by the harmonic function of time $y = 0.01 \cos \omega_F t$ m.

Determine for steady-state vibrations:

(a)   the value of the frequency ω_F for the vibrating support when body 1 (of mass 1 kg) is stationary, and

(b)   the amplitude of vibration of body 2 (of mass 2 kg) when body 1 is stationary.

Answers   (a) 1.007 Hz (b) 5 mm.

6.15   Consider again the system shown in Figure 6.35. In this case $m_1 = 1$ kg, $m_2 = 2$ kg, $k_1 = 40$ N/m and $k_2 = 80$ N/m. The plate P vibrates with a frequency four times that of the lower value ω_1 of the circular natural frequencies of vibration of the system and with amplitude 10 mm, i.e., $y = 0.01 \cos \omega_F t$ m, where $\omega_F = 4\omega_1$.

Derive expressions for the displacements of the two bodies after

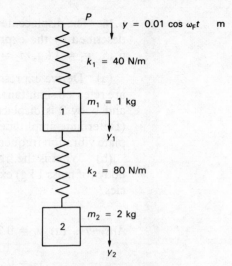

P

$y = 0.01 \cos \omega_F t$ m

$k_1 = 40$ N/m

1   $m_1 = 1$ kg

y_1

$k_2 = 80$ N/m

2   $m_2 = 2$ kg

y_2

Figure 6.35   Diagram for Problems 6.14–6.16.

both bodies are released simultaneously at $t = 0$ when body 1 is held in the equilibrium position and body 2 is displaced 20 cm from the equilibrium position. Hence determine the positions of both bodies in relation to their equilibrium positions three seconds after their release.

Answers $y_1 = A_1 \cos \omega_1 t + C_1 \cos \omega_2 t$
$\qquad + \{0.01 k_1 (k_2 - m_2 \omega_F^2)/D\} \cos \omega_F t,$
$\qquad y_2 = \{k_2 A_1/(k_2 - m_2 \omega_1^2)\} \cos \omega_1 t$
$\qquad + \{k_2 C_1/(k_2 - m_2 \omega_2^2)\} \cos \omega_2 t$
$\qquad + \{0.01 k_1 k_2/D\} \cos \omega_F t,$

where
$D = (k_1 + k_2 - m_1 \omega_F^2)(k_2 - m_2 \omega_F^2) - k_2^2,$
$A_1 = 0.2(k_2 - m_2 \omega_1^2)(k_2 - m_2 \omega_2^2)/\{k_2 m_2 (\omega_1^2 - \omega_2^2)\}$
$\qquad + 0.01 k_1 (\omega_2^2 - \omega_F^2)(k_2 - m_2 \omega_1^2)/E,$
$C_1 = -0.01 k_1 (k_2 - m_2 \omega_F^2)/D$
$\qquad - 0.2(k_2 - m_2 \omega_1^2)(k_2 - m_2 \omega_2^2)/\{k_2 m_2 (\omega_1^2 - \omega_2^2)\}$
$\qquad - 0.01 k_1 (\omega_2^2 - \omega_F^2)(k_2 - m_2 \omega_1^2)/E,$ and
$E = (\omega_1^2 - \omega_2^2)\{(k_1 + k_2 - m_1 \omega_F^2)(k_2 - m_2 \omega_F^2) - k_2^2\}$

Hence,
$y_1 = 0.1160 \cos (3.274t) - 0.1013 \cos (12.218t)$
$\qquad - 0.0147 \cos (13.095t) \,[\text{m}]$
$y_2 = 0.1584 \cos (3.274t) + 0.0371 \cos (12.218t)$
$\qquad + 0.0045 \cos (13.095t) \,[\text{m}];$

body 1 is 157.6 mm above its equilibrium position and body 2 is 127.5 mm above its equilibrium position.

Note that in this problem, because one body is not at the equilibrium position at $t = 0$, the transient solution has to be included for y_1 and y_2. With damping in the system the transient solution (the first two terms in y_1 and y_2) would quickly die away to zero.

6.16 The displacement of the vibrating plate P (see Figure 6.35) is described by the expression $y_F = 0.2 \cos \omega_F t$ m. As for problem 6.15, $m_1 = 1$ kg, $m_2 = 2$ kg, $k_1 = 40$ N/m and $k_2 = 80$ N/m.

(a) Derive expressions for the displacements after both bodies are released simultaneously at $t = 0$ when body 1 is displaced 20 cm and body 2 is displaced 40 cm from their equilibrium positions. (Determine amplitudes to an accuracy of 1 mm.) Assume that the plate vibration frequency is given by $\omega_F = 10$ rad/s.

(b) What is the frequency of the vibrating plate when the first body (of mass 1 kg) executes vibration only at the natural frequencies?

Answers (a) $y_1 = 0.292 \cos (3.274t) - 0.201 \cos (12.218t)$
$\qquad\qquad + 0.109 \cos (10t)$
$\qquad y_2 = 0.399 \cos (3.274t) + 0.074 \cos (12.218t)$
$\qquad\qquad - 0.073 \cos (10t)$

(b) 6.325 rad/s.
Note that in this problem the transient solution must be considered as well as the steady-state solution.

6.17 A trailer consists of a body supported by springs upon an axle having two wheels. The mass of the trailer body is 360 kg. The axle and wheel assembly have a mass of 90 kg. The total stiffness of the suspension springs is 72 kN/m and the total stiffness of the tyres is 180 kN/m. The trailer is pulled along a level road which has a sinusoidal surface of wavelength 3 m and amplitude 25 mm.
Determine:

(a) the critical speeds of the trailer,
(b) the speed at which the axle will have no vertical steady-state motion, and
(c) the amplitude of steady-state motion of the trailer body when it is travelling at 13 m/s.

Answers (a) 5.65, 25.53 m/s (b) 6.75 m/s (c) 7.8 mm.

6.18 A uniform, light elastic shaft of circular cross-section can be regarded as being simply supported in its bearings. It is loaded with two rotors as shown in Figure 6.36. The diameter of the shaft is 50 mm and Young's modulus for the material of the shaft is 210 GPa.
Determine the two natural frequencies of the system using an exact method.

Answers 3.61 and 13.36 Hz.

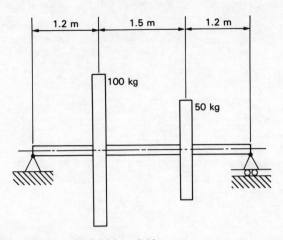

Figure 6.36   Diagram for Problem 6.18.

6.19   A floor is to support two heavy machines, one of mass 1000 kg at a point A, and another of mass 2000 kg at a point B. The elastic properties of the floor are such that when a load of mass 500 kg is placed at A, the deflections at A and B are, respectively, 8 mm and 3 mm; when a load of mass 500 kg is placed at B the deflection at B is 5 mm.

Neglecting the mass of the floor, determine the natural frequencies of vibration of the floor when both machines are in position.

Answers   3.05 and 5.17 Hz.

Index